ISSUES I

C000132741

HEALTH AND
WELFARE

ISSUES IN SOCIOLOGY

Edited by Robin Oakley

HEALTH
AND
WELFARE

Hilary Graham

Macmillan Education

First published in 1985

Published by
MACMILLAN EDUCATION LTD
Houndmills, Basingstoke, Hampshire RG21 2XS
and London
Companies and representatives
throughout the world

Typeset by Columns of Reading
Printed in Hong Kong

British Library Cataloguing in Publication Data
Graham, Hilary
Health and welfare.—(Issues in sociology)
1. Public welfare—Great Britain
I. Title II. Series
361.6'0941   HV245
ISBN 0–333–37191–7

Contents

Editor's Preface

This book forms part of a series entitled Issues in Sociology which is designed for students on A Level and other similar courses in schools and colleges.

The series consists of a set of relatively short books, intended for personal use by the student, which can provide a more flexible and stimulating programme of study than can be offered by the conventional textbook alone.

Each book covers one key substantive area of current A Level syllabuses. The series aims particularly to cover those topics that are new and popular, or those that are inadequately provided for in existing texts. It also provides a different approach from that of the textbook in that, rather than being presented with a digest of sociological literature and concerns, students will confront a selection of original extracts from such literature which they will analyse and assess for themselves. The aim is to emphasise the nature of sociological enquiry and debate and to encourage students to interpret and assess the evidence and arguments put forward.

The intention of this series, therefore, is not to replace the textbook approach but rather to supplement and extend it.

The author's introduction outlines the field of study covered by the book, placing it in its wider context and highlighting a number of general issues and problems. Each chapter consists primarily of a series of documentary extracts focusing on a particular issue or area of debate and a short introduction sets out a framework within which the students can read and analyse the material presented. Each extract is selected to illustrate a particular source of data or perspective and to complement each by providing alternative views or contrasting evidence.

Questions are supplied that test the full range of skills from comprehension of specific extracts to synthesis and appraisal of a range of literature as required in essay questions in A Level and equivalent examinations.

Finally, there is a list of references for parallel or follow-up reading by students at the end of each chapter.

R.O.

Acknowledgements

In introducing the arguments about health and welfare, I have drawn on the work and the ideas of many people. The list of references and the bibliography at the back of the book record my debt to them. In addition, I would like to thank Jim Kincaid and Marilyn Lawrence for their comments on a draft of *Health and Welfare*. The book is the better for their criticisms; I, needless to say, bear responsibility for the faults that remain. Sue How typed the book in its various stages. My special thanks go to her.

H.G.

The author and publishers wish to thank the following who have kindly given permission for the use of copyright material:

George Allen & Unwin (Publishers) Ltd for extracts from *Unmasking Medicine* by Ian Kennedy; *Strategy of Inequality* by J. Le Grand; *Commitment to Welfare* by Richard M. Titmuss; and *Gift Relationship: from Human Blood to Social Policy* by Richard M. Titmuss.

American Psychological Association for an extract from an article by T. Szasz in *American Psychologist* (1960).

Associated Book Publishers Ltd for extracts from *An Introduction to Medical Sociology* (1976) by D. Tuckett; 'Depression: a sociological view' by George Brown in *Basic Readings in Medical Sociology* (1978) edited by D. Tuckett and J. Kaufert; and *Infant Mortality: a Social Problem* by G. Newman.

Basil Blackwell Ltd for extracts from *The Role of Medicine* by Thomas McKeown; and *Aspects of Illness* by R. Dingwall.

Marion Boyars Publishers Ltd for an extract from *Limits to Medicine: Medical Nemesis, the Expropriation of Health* by Ivan Illich.

Brent Community Health Council for an extract from *Black People and the Health Service*.

British Medical Journal for an extract from 'International perspectives on the NHS' by R. Klein, in *British Medical Journal* (1977).

The Controller of Her Majesty's Stationery Office for extracts from *Prevention and Health* (1977); the *Royal Commission on the National Health Service* (1979); and *Inequalities in Health* by P. Townsend and N. Davidson.

Equal Opportunities Commission for an extract from *Caring for the Elderly and Handicapped: Community Care Policies and Women's Lives* (1982).

Family Policy Studies Centre for an extract from *Whose Child?* by Valerie McLeod.

Heinemann Educational Books for condensed extracts from *After the New Right* by N. Bosanquet; and for extracts from *The Future of the Welfare State* edited by Howard Glennerster: The Fabian Society.

Dr R. Holman for an extract from his essay 'Another model of poverty' in *Social Welfare in Modern Britain* edited by Eric Butterworth and David Weir.

Hughes Massie Ltd on behalf of Oscar Lewis for an extract from *La Vida*.

Institute of Economic Affairs for extracts from *Wither the Welfare State* by A. Seldon; and 'Economic effects of moral hazard' by R. Harris in *The Moral Hazard of Social Benefits* by H. Parker.

Michael Joseph Ltd for an extract from *The Evolution of National Insurance in Great Britain* by B. Gilbert.

Longman Group Ltd for an extract from *The Family and the State* by R. Moroney.

National Council for Voluntary Organisations, Bedford Square Press, for an extract from *In Worlds Apart: Professions and their Clients in the Welfare State* (1978) by T. Robinson.

Office of Population Censuses and Surveys for an extract from Occasional Paper 31, *The Family*.

Organisation for Economic Co-operation and Development for an extract from a table in *Economic Outlook* (July 1983).

Penguin Books Ltd for extracts from *Poverty and Equality in Britain* by J.C. Kincaid (Pelican Books, revised edition 1975) and from *Working Class Wives* by Margery Spring Rice (Penguin Books, 1939).

Pluto Press for an extract from 'A matter of life and death: medicine, health and statistics' by L. Doyal in *Demystifying Social Statistics* by J. Irvine, I. Miles and J. Evans.

Routledge & Kegan Paul PLC for extracts from 'Measuring poverty' by Peter Townsend from *The British Journal of Sociology* (1954); *The Sex Role System* by J. Chetwynd and O. Hartnett (1978); *The Receiving End: Consumer Accounts of Social Help for Children* by N. Timms (1973); *The Client Speaks: Working Class Impressions of Casework* by J.E. Mayer and N. Timms (1970); and *A Labour of Love: Women, Work and Caring* by J. Finch and D. Groves (1983).

Joseph Rowntree Charitable Trust for an extract from *Poverty and Progress* by B.S. Rowntree.

The University of Chicago Press for an extract from *Capitalism and Freedom* by M. Friedman.

Questions from past examination papers have been kindly supplied by the following boards: Associated Examining Board; Joint Matriculation Board; University of London; and University of Oxford Delegacy of Local Examinations.

Every effort has been made to trace all the copyright holders but if any have been inadvertently overlooked the publishers will be pleased to make the necessary arrangements at the first opportunity.

Introduction

This introduction has two purposes. First, it explains why sociologists have taken such a keen interest in health and welfare, highlighting why now, in a period of rapid social and economic change in Britain, questions of health and welfare are becoming increasingly central to sociology. This is the focus of the first part of the introduction. Secondly, the introduction outlines the content of the book. It describes briefly the controversies that each chapter addresses and ends by identifying the more general issues which underlie these areas of controversy.

The answer to the question of why sociologists study health and welfare lies in their concern with the question of social stability and social change. Sociology has long been interested in how societies remain stable at a time of social upheaval. Its interest has focused on the development of capitalism in Britain, Western Europe and the United States and the way in which these societies have accommodated an industrial revolution without a breakdown in the social order. In their search for an understanding of how capitalist societies have managed to combine social integration with social change, sociologists have turned to the field of health and welfare. The sociology of health and welfare has offered two kinds of insights.

First, sociologists have needed sensitive indicators to measure the social consequences of economic development. Health and welfare have served as such indicators, with statistics on infant mortality and poverty measuring the impact of capitalism on the people. In the eighteenth and nineteenth centuries, the signs of increased prosperity in Britain led economists to conclude that capitalism promoted greater harmony and well-being for the majority of the population. In the late nineteenth century, it was the evidence of poor health and living conditions among the British working class which alerted the early empirical sociologists, Charles Booth and Seebohm Rowntree, to the less acceptable face of British capitalism. And it was the spectre of mass poverty which provided fuel for the theories of Karl Marx. Similarly, today, social scientists look to the health and welfare of the people for evidence by which to assess the characters of western capitalism. Today's assessments, however, relate not only to the market economy. Statistics on ill-health and poverty are seen to reflect, too, the impact of the welfare state on the people of Britain.

The question of health and welfare has been central to

1

sociology in a second respect. How governments have responded to illness and destitution is seen as crucial to their success in maintaining social order. Public spending on welfare services – health care, education, housing and income support – only began on a significant scale in the late nineteenth century, and large welfare budgets are unique to the late twentieth century. The growth of a welfare state, in Britain and elsewhere, has led sociologists to speculate whether welfare spending is a mechanism by which capitalist societies survive.

In focusing on these two sets of questions – about the distribution of health and welfare and about the role of the welfare state in promoting social stability – sociologists have confronted the existence of social inequality. While governments have spent more on welfare services, sociologists have continued to uncover persistent differences in the life-chances and living standards of different groups in the community. The data on ill-health and poverty indicate that, while we are all better off than we were 100 years ago, inequalities are as pronounced as ever. The inequalities, moreover, appear to follow the contours of our social structure. Good health is thus an indicator of wealth and privilege; poor health reflects poverty and powerlessness. It is in the experience of health and welfare that the social divisions of class, gender, race and age take on their human shape.

The debate about inequality and social policy has intensified over the last decade. Economic recession, technological change and an ageing population have increased the number of people dependent on the welfare state for their survival. Yet, at the same time, Britain has elected a Conservative government committed to reducing the role of the state in the provision of services. Now, as in the nineteenth century, social scientists are asking some basic questions about health and welfare. It is these questions which are addressed in the eight chapters of this book. Its coverage, however, is inevitably selective. It aims only to give a sense of the shape of the debate: the detail can be found in the further readings, listed at the end of each chapter.

This brings us to the second aim of the introduction: to give an indication of what the book contains. The opening three chapters examine the controversy surrounding the nature and causes of poverty and ill-health. The fourth and fifth chapters move on to consider the debate about the organisation of welfare services: how the welfare state treats those it serves and whether its activities promote social equality in an efficient and cost-effective way. Chapter 6 looks more broadly at the relation between the welfare state and capitalism. It considers a number of major perspectives which provide very different accounts of the nature of social policy and the part it plays in maintaining social divisions. Chapter 7 looks at the debate about the family in more detail, describing how social scientists view the role of the family in health care. The final chapter, Chapter 8, looks to the future and considers the major policy options at present being considered for health and welfare.

Reading through the debates reviewed in this book, it is possible to detect a number of underlying issues which fuel much of the controversy. These issues are often obscured in the detail of sociological studies, as they delve deep into the statistics on poverty and the intricacies of doctor–patient interaction. Making these issues explicit at the outset may help with the difficult task of deciding what the argument is really all about.

Four issues can usefully be identified. First, there is the fundamental question of what kind of society Britain (or any other country) wants to build. What are its central values: freedom, equality, democracy? What do these values mean in policy terms? Are they reconcilable?

Secondly, what is the nature of the capitalist economy? How does it distribute the rewards of industrial progress among its people? How does it relate to the traditional divisions between 'men's work' and 'women's work': does capitalism reinforce or undermine the nuclear family? How does it relate to racial divisions? Does it reinforce white power? With these considerations in mind, does capitalism provide an adequate foundation for the preservation of freedom, equality and democracy?

Thirdly, what are the causes of 'the ugly face of capitalism': what causes poverty, unemployment, ill-health and the wider inequalities of social class, race, sex and region? Are these signs of suffering the result of deficiencies among individuals: a lack of intelligence perhaps, or moral discipline? Or are they the result of systematic differences in society: differences in access to employment, education, health care and housing?

Fourthly, what is the nature of the welfare state? Does it support or threaten the economic system in which it developed? Is it an agent of care or social control? Has it reduced illness and economic hardship or increased them? Does it seek to promote social equality at the cost of individual freedom?

These four issues run through much of the material discussed in this book. They surface most clearly in the final chapter, concerned with perhaps the most important debate within the sociology of health and welfare: what kind of welfare state should Britain be building for the twenty-first century?

Further Reading

1. M. Hill, *Understanding Social Policy*, Basil Blackwell/Martin Robertson, 1980, Chapter 2, 'The growth of social policy'.

2. B. Abel Smith, 'Assessing the balance sheet' in H. Glennerster (ed), *The Future of the Welfare State*, Heinemann, 1983.

3. P.Thane, *The Foundations of the Welfare State*, Longman, 1982, Chapter 9, 'Assessment'.

4. New Society Social Studies Readers, *The Origins of the Social Services*, and *The Growth of the Social Services*, New Society, 1983.

1
What is health?
What is welfare?

INTRODUCTION

In the Introduction, we noted that the concepts of health and welfare are deeply woven into the sociological debate about the nature of capitalism and the welfare state. This chapter, and the two that follow, examine these concepts. The present chapter focuses on the ways sociologists have defined and measured health and welfare.

Defining terms in sociology is rarely an easy task. First, definitions tend to involve explanations. The way sociologists define health and welfare is closely related to their theories about the causes of these conditions. Secondly, definitions are not only linked to explanations, they tend to be linked to political perspectives. It is possible to attach the labels of Right and Left, Conservative and Socialist to the scientific models that sociologists have evolved in their study of health and welfare. Sociologists have been accused of taking sides, with one model aligned to the managerial interest of doctors and social workers, the other articulating the experiences of the sick and the poor. In defining health and welfare, sociologists are seen (and often see themselves) as making moral as well as scientific evaluations.

There are three other problems, however, which are more particular to the study of health and welfare. First, the concepts have traditionally been defined negatively. Sociologists have approached the question of health through the concept of *illness*; they have measured welfare through the concept of *poverty*. Secondly, definitions in the field of health and welfare tend to be confusingly similar. The World Health Organisation defines health as 'a state of complete physical, mental and social wellbeing' while the Oxford English Dictionary defines welfare as 'the state or condition of being well'. Replacing these concepts with those of poverty and illness does not help much either. Poverty, as defined officially by the state, is an income level below that needed to sustain health. This close association between poverty and ill-health is one that is not always apparent, however. To appreciate its invisibility, we must introduce a third feature of the debate about health and welfare. Social scientists have concerned themselves traditionally with the welfare of

5

families, by looking at the position of the husband/father. The well-being of other family members thus becomes what Seebohm Rowntree identified as one of 'the things that are not seen'. As he notes, 'we *see* that many a labourer, who has a wife and three or four children is healthy and a good worker, although he only earns a pound a week. What we do *not see* is that in order to give him enough food, mother and children go short, for the mother knows that all depends upon the wages of her husband' (Seebohm Rowntree, *Poverty: A Study in Town Life*, p. 135).

With these points in mind, we will consider the debate about definitions in the fields of health and welfare.

DEFINING AND MEASURING HEALTH

The controversy about health is generally represented as a battle between two models of health: the social model and the medical model. These two models should be seen as ideal types: in fact, it is difficult to find a social scientist who publically defends 'the medical model' in its pure form.

The medical model views health as the absence of illness and disability. It defines health in negative terms, as 'not sickness', with illness and disability seen as physical conditions whose existence can be established by medical diagnosis. Since the presence of illness can be established objectively, through diagnosis, 'health' and 'illness' are taken to be objective categories. It is not social meanings which create ill-health, but malfunctions in the body. The spotlight can therefore be on the individual alone. It is this model of health which is seen by sociologists to underline the development of Western medical practice since the Renaissance, and, since 1948, the development of the National Health Service.

The features of this medical model are summarised in the reading below. (Electroencephalograph readings are commonly known as EEGs, which provide a reading of brain-cell activity. Biopsies involve the removal of a portion of living tissue for examination.)

Reading 1

[In this model] the characteristics that define specific disease refer to biological processes. Information is gathered by means of indicators like X-rays, blood sugar levels, electroencephalograph readings or biopsies, which are thought to tap these biological processes directly. This framework is, then, closely associated with developments in Western science . . . Physicians can readily reach a consensus on the operation of body systems by reference to well-defined criteria which are generally familiar to members of the medical profession and which become progressively sharper with advances in scientific knowledge. Differences of opinion are matters that will eventually be superseded by advances in knowledge. A feature of this advance . . . is the gradual elimination of verbal reports as either necessary or sufficient for diagnosis and the aim of biological scientists of dispensing with them altogether: instead of having to rely on subjective verbal reports of symptoms, the medical practitioner will be able to use signs derived from objective indices of biological structure or function – regardless of whether the supposed patient actually feels ill.

Viewed in this light, specific diseases can be said to be universal. If the current norms used by physicians to judge biological functioning are reliable and valid, then any indication of a deviation is *prima facie* evidence of disease.

R. Dingwall, *Aspects of Illness*, 1976, pp. 45–6.

Questions

1. *What are the main features of the medical model? How is the presence of disease established?*
2. *What is meant by 'subjective verbal reports of symptoms'? What role do they play in diagnosis?*
3. *What do you think the author means when he says that the medical model is 'closely associated with developments in Western science'?*
4. *In what ways do you think the National Health Service reflects the influence of the medical model?*

In the next extract, Ian Kennedy launches a major attack on the medical model. He challenges the idea that illness is 'a matter of objective scientific fact'. He asserts, instead, that it is a status ascribed by those in a position of power. This alternative perspective is associated with the social model of health. In this model, health is seen as a relative condition: it implies some socially-agreed norm against which deviations can be identified and labelled. What is defined as health varies over time and between cultures. It is also likely to vary between individuals in the same culture. While not denying that physical disorder and mental suffering are real, the social model highlights the way in which the meaning of disorder and the experience of suffering are socially constructed. Sociologists sometimes use the terms 'disease' and 'illness' to distinguish between the physical and social dimensions of ill-health. 'Disease' exists when there is a clinical disorder, but it only earns the label 'illness' when it is recognised and treated as such by the individual. It is the nature of this label that concerns Ian Kennedy.

Reading 2

To analyse the word 'illness' is to explore the role of the doctor in modern medicine. It is to discover that medical practice is, above all, a political enterprise, one in which judgements about people are made . . .

We all agree that someone with an inflamed appendix is ill. Why do we all agree? It's obvious, you say. Someone with an inflamed appendix *is* ill. He's got appendicitis. But this is a circular argument. We have to go more carefully. What we have are certain facts about the physical condition of a person. We all agree that these are illnesses because we accept two propositions. The first is that there is a normal state in which the appendix is not inflamed . . . Secondly, it is appropriate to judge someone who deviates from this norm as ill. Only if we examine both of these will we understand what is involved in the meaning of the word 'illness'.

Take the first of the two propositions, that there must be a deviation from the normal state. This seems simple enough. It isn't, of course. For a start, it's only our convention to call such deviations illness . . . Others in other cultures may view such conditions entirely differently. They may see them as visitations from the gods, as punishments deserved and to be accepted, or as possession by spirits. We cleave to science and the scientific principle of a demonstrable state of normality and a causative agent which brings about an abnormality. Few would object to this convention. Even so, we still have a problem. What is the state we should regard as normal? . . .

What is the normal state against which to measure abnormality is a product of social and cultural values and expectations. It is not some static, objectively identifiable fact. As views and values change, so the norm will change. So, if illness has as its first criterion some deviation from the norm, some abnormality, it too will vary and change in its meaning . . .

So illness, a central concept of medicine, is not a matter of objective scientific fact. Instead, it's a term used to describe deviation from a notional norm. So a choice exists whether to call someone ill. The choice depends upon the norm chosen, and this is a matter of social and political judgement . . . Ordinarily, there will be wide-spread agreement about what objective facts, what physical states are appropriately described as abnormal. But this does not belie the fact that there is an inherent vagueness in the term 'illness'. And this is only the beginning. Even when it has been decided that the physical conditions warrant the description 'abnormal', there is still the second step. They have to be judged to be an illness. An evaluation has to take place.

Just because illness is associated with objective facts, it appears that illness is those facts, that illness is a thing. But as we've seen, illness is not a thing; it's a judgemental term. Being ill is not a state; it's a status, to be granted or withheld by those who have the power to do so. Status connotes a particular position in society, assumed only after satisfying others that certain conditions have been observed.

I. Kennedy, *Unmasking Medicine*, 1981, pp. 2–4, 7–8.

Questions
1. *Identify the central features of Kennedy's perspective on illness. Do you think his perspective is correct?*
2. *How does Kennedy characterise the practice of modern medicine? How might a doctor respond to this characterisation?*
3. *The author places much weight on the concept of deviation. What does he mean by this concept?*

While the author of Reading 2 employs a social model of health in his critique of medicine, the model remains implicit. Reading 3 explores the model in more detail. In providing a more complex account of the social model, it challenges as over-simplistic Kennedy's view that illness is a label ascribed by doctors. It looks at individuals in their social context, arguing that 'seeing the doctor' is only one possible outcome to the experience of being unwell.

Reading 3
'I wish I knew what you mean by being sick. Sometimes I felt so bad I could curl up and die, but I had to go on becuase of the kids who have to be taken care of, and besides, we didn't have the money to spend for the doctor. How could I be sick? Some people can be sick anytime with anything, but most of us can't be sick, even when we need to be.'[1]

This articulate woman makes the point that 'illness' is defined according to a set of values and norms – the point at which an individual ceases to fulfil obligations, feels his life is not satisfactory, feels he cannot do what he wants, depends in part on the situations he is in and the norms and values that are attached to different behaviours. The quotation also suggests another point, there seem to be two stages involved in seeking medical care: recognizing that one is 'ill', and then deciding to do something about it . . .

For symptoms, which are recognized by the medical profession as signs of disease, to be taken to the doctor they must first be perceived as a problem, then defined as something to be taken to the doctor, and then actually taken there. This process of *recognition*, *definition*, and *action* can, of course, be influenced in a powerful way by members of the individual's family or others in a position close to him. Symptoms can be other, as well as, self defined. Looking at the large number of symptoms experienced by people who are not in care, it seems that the majority of individuals do not necessarily define as problems symptoms that most doctors would identify as pathological . . .

The evidence . . . suggests a pattern of ongoing accommodation to symptoms within the community that is only rarely interrupted by seeking medical aid. However, this does not mean that individuals never go to see their doctors or experience being a patient. On average, men in the UK made about three visits, and women about four, during the year studied by Dunnell and Cartwright[2] . . . What does happen, however, is that individuals only present their doctors with some of their symptoms. . . . It is also worth remembering that the epidemiological evidence suggests that the symptoms that are taken for help are not necessarily those that a doctor would consider the most serious . . .

It seems that a considerable accommodation can develop between individuals, their symptoms, and the patterns of relationships and activities they are involved in. Recognizing this Zola[3] argued that to understand a visit to the doctor it is necesary to consider what can lead to a breakdown in his accommodation.

'Virtually every day of our lives we are subjected to a vast array of discomforts. Only an infinitesimal amount of these get to a physician. Neither the mere presence nor the obviousness of symptoms, neither their medical seriousness nor objective discomfort seems to differentiate the episodes which do and do not get professional treatment. In short, what then does convert a person to a patient? . . .' (Zola 1973: 678–9)

The author's basic claim is that the decision to seek medical aid was based on a break in the accommodation to symptoms and did not necessarily occur at the point where the individual felt most ill . . .

Further studies will need to replicate and extend the work before it will have significant implications. What does become clear is that individuals ceased to cope with symptoms themselves and started to define themselves as patients, or be defined by others, because of the inability of the social and interpersonal network in which they were involved to contain them. The definition of a problem as one requiring medical attention was inextricably bound up with changes in the patient's social and emotional environment. The implication is striking: action directed at allowing the network to accommodate the symptoms, or some change in the network's ability to do so, can remove the need for a visit. In fact, many visits to the doctor may be as much about the social and interpersonal network in which a patient is located as about the symptoms which . . . need be no more than a presenting complaint, a ticket to obtain help with difficulties of a social, interpersonal, or emotional kind.

1. E. Koos, *The Health of Regionsville*, Columbia University Press, 1954.
2. K. Dunnell and A. Cartwright (1982), *Medicine Takers, Prescribers and Hoarders*, London: Routledge & Kegan Paul, 1982.
3. I. Zola, 'Pathways to the Doctor: From Person to Patient', *Social Science and Medicine*, 1973, 7: 677–89.

   D. Tuckett, *An Introduction to Medical Sociology*, 1976, pp. 161, 164, 174, 176–7, 179.

Questions

1. *What are the main features of the social model of health? How is the presence of illness established?*
2. *What is meant by 'accommodation to symptoms'? What is meant by 'the social and interpersonal network'? What are the implications of the concepts of 'accommodation' and 'network' for our understanding of illness?*
3. *The woman in the extract asks the sociologist 'I wish I knew what you mean by being sick.' What answer does the author provide?*
4. *Describe the process by which a person becomes a patient.*

The final extract in this section turns from the question of definition to the question of measurement. While sociologists are increasingly turning to a social model of health, statistics are collected within the framework of the medical model. As the author of the extract suggests, statistics on health in fact tell us how many people are certified as 'not well'. Moreover, since most statistics are generated by the medical profession, they tend to tell us as much about the nature and scope of our medical services as about the nature and incidence of ill-health.

Reading 4

The first point to be made here is the quite outstanding *lack* of available information on health and illness. We know very little indeed about the health problems of the British people. Although a survey of sickness was carried out from 1944 to 1952, this was discontinued, so that no continuous national survey of health and illness is now available. This makes it very difficult either to assess historical trends in health and illness, or to obtain any reliable asessment of contemporary problems of ill-health. This lack of statistics on general well-being or illness reflects the narrow orientation of existing health statistics. We can only *infer* levels of health and illness from statistics produced for other purposes. These fall into four major categories: 1. mortality statistics; 2. statistics on the utilisation of the NHS; 3. sickness absence statistics; and 4. information collected from the *General Household Survey*. Let us examine each of these in turn.

Mortality statistics are regarded as an essential element in any set of national statistics and are therefore produced on a regular and reliable basis . . . Infant mortality rates in particular are regarded as being among the most sensitive indicators of the material conditions of a given population. However, mortality statistics are obviously only crude indicators of the state of health of those people who remain alive. Although there are diseases where high levels of morbidity are always associated with high levels of mortality, there are many other diseases where chronic and debilitating symptoms are not associated with high levels of mortality.

In the case of *statistics on the use of health facilities*, we are really dealing with two sets of data. First, there are *ad hoc* studies of the use of particular facilities (e.g. General Practitioner morbidity studies) and, second, there are various sets of statistics generated within the NHS bureaucracy (e.g. Hospital In-Patient

Enquiry – HIPE). But such sources suffer from the basic problem that they only deal with the people who come into contact with the medical care system, which obviously limits their use as indicators of general patterns of morbidity. From these statistics we will know that certain people seek medical care for certain *specific* medical conditions, but we will know nothing about those cases of ill-health which were not brought to the attention of a doctor and were therefore not officially recorded.

In addition, of course, we cannot assess the relationship between the patient's *actual* condition, and the way in which the doctor has labelled it. Doctors have to find some definition within the bounds of scientific medicine to categorise the condition of the patient in front of them . . . This definitional problem is at its most acute when we arrive at the end of the 'illness' spectrum labelled 'mental illness' . . . Much critical work exists on the problem of psychiatric classification and diagnosis, documenting at its most simple level the extreme variability in diagnosis between different psychiatrists confronted with the same patients. Such work throws into doubt the utility of statistics, generated in terms of standard psychiatric diagnostic categories, for telling us very much about the patients concerned. What the statistics *do* show, however, is the ever-increasing number of people receiving psychiatric treatment, and in particular, the numbers actually entering hospital, and how long they stay . . .

A third source of data on the health status of the population comes from the *statistics on sickness absence from work* produced by the DHSS. These concern the payments of sickness benefit and are regularly produced since they are of obvious bureaucratic value. However, as a source of information on the health of the general population, they are again very limited. First, while they cover almost all men of working age (but *not*, of course, the unemployed) they exclude all women not involved in full-time paid employment, as well as the majority of working women who until the Social Security Act of 1975 were able to opt out of the social security system by paying a 'married woman's stamp'. In addition, they of course exclude by definition all those above and below working age. Furthermore, sickness absence statistics do not cover any periods of sickness absence which last less than three days,* since such short absences do not entitle the patient to sickness benefit . . .

The final source from which we can infer levels of health and illness in the population is the *General Household Survey* (GHS),

undertaken continuously for the DHSS by the Office of
Population Censuses and Surveys. The GHS asks several
questions relating to morbidity, including questions concerning
acute sickness, long-standing illness and days off work. Long-
standing illness is established by asking respondents whether or
not they suffer from any illness which limits their activities
compared with people of their own age. Alternatively, acute
sickness is defined as sickness or injury which results in
restrictions on normal activity at any time during the two weeks
before interview. Data obtained from such a survey have the
limitations of any survey data. In particular, they underestimate
problems such as cancer or mental illness. However, assessing
morbidity levels on the basis of the GHS data clearly avoids the
more serious problems encountered in the use of health
utilisation and sickness absence statistics – in that respondents
are themselves asked about their health. For this reason, it can
probably be regarded as the least unsatisfactory estimate of the
state of health of the population.

   *   from April 1 1982 – 7 days.
       L. Doyal, 'A matter of life and death: medicine, health and
       statistics' in J. Irvine, I. Miles and J. Evans (eds), *Demystifying
       Social Statistics*, 1979, pp. 241–6.

Questions

1. *Describe the four main types of statistics. In what ways do they reflect a
   medical model of health?*
2. *According to the author of Reading 4, 'mortality statistics are regarded
   as an essential element in any national statistics'. The table on p. 15 is
   reproduced from the Bills of Mortality for London for the year 1665.
   What problems does it highlight about the use of such statistics in
   measuring health?*
3. *What indicators might better reflect the health of the population than
   those used at present? What kind of statistics would be compatible with
   the social model of health?*
4. *Using the material contained in all four extracts, identify from within
   the pairs listed below, the terms you would associate with a medical
   and a social perspective on health.*
      positive / negative
      objective / subjective
      social / individual
      curative medicine / preventive medicine
      absolute / relative
      lay / professional

The Diseases and Casualties this Week.

		Imposthume	11
		Infants	16
		Killed by a fall from the Belfrey at Alhallows the Great	1
		Kingsevil	2
		Lethargy	1
		Palsie	1
		Plague	7165
Abortive	5	Rickets	17
Aged	43	Rising of the Lights	11
Ague	2	Scowring	5
Apoplexie	1	Scurvy	2
Bleeding	2	Spleen	1
Burnt in his Bed by a Candle at St. Giles Cripplegate	1	Spotted Feaver	101
		Stilborn	17
Canker	1	Stone	2
Childbed	42	Stopping of the stomach	9
Chrisomes	18	Strangury	1
Consumption	134	Suddenly	1
Convulsion	64	Surfeit	49
Cough	2	Teeth	121
Dropsie	33	Thrush	5
Feaver	309	Timpany	1
Flox and Small-pox	5	Tissick	11
Frighted	3	Vomiting	3
Gowt	1	Winde	3
Grief	3	Wormes	15
Griping in the Guts	51		
Jaundies	5		

Christned ⎰ Males — 95, Females — 81, In all — 176 ⎱   Buried ⎰ Males — 4095, Females — 4202, In all — 8297 ⎱ Plague — 7165

Increased in the Burials this Week — 607

Parishes clear of the Plague — 4   Parishes Infected — 126

The Assize of Bread set forth by Order of the Lord Maior and Court of Aldermen, A penny Wheaten Loaf to contain Nine Ounces and a half, and three half-penny White Loaves the like weight.

Museum of London

DEFINING AND MEASURING POVERTY

The controversies surrounding the nature of poverty in many respects parallel those identified in relation to health. While poverty has been seen in different ways at different periods in Britain's history, today's debate is dominated by two perspectives.

The first, dating back to the eighteenth and nineteenth centuries, links welfare to the idea of subsistence. The poor are those whose income is insufficient to buy the food and shelter necessary to keep them healthy (and keep them working). Those above this 'poverty line' are presumed to have enough money to meet their physical needs and maintain their physical capacity.

The extract below, taken from the work of Seebohm Rowntree, is seen by many to represent the ideal type of this absolute conception of poverty. Yet Rowntree recognised that his concept of absolute or primary poverty had many inadequacies. As he notes, there is little opportunity for the expression of social and cultural needs on the poverty line (identified in the category of 'sundries' in Reading 5). He acknowledges, too, that this model does not take account of the way social custom dictates patterns of spending on physical needs for food, clothing, housing and fuel. Despite these reservations, Rowntree's calculations served to mark the boundary between welfare and poverty in Beveridge's plans for Britain's post-war welfare state. Beveridge recommended a level of state benefits designed to ensure that the vulnerable sections of the population would remain, however marginally, 'in welfare'.

Reading 5

My primary poverty line represented the minimum sum on which physical efficiency could be maintained. It was a standard of bare *subsistence* rather than *living*. The figure for food was arrived at by translating into a diet the minimum amount of nutriment, expressed in terms of fats, carbohydrates and protein, which the leading physiologists of the day regarded as necessary for physical efficiency. The dietary [i.e. diet] I selected was more economical and less attractive than was given to paupers in workhouses. I purposely selected such a dietary so that no one could possibly accuse me of placing my subsistence level too high. All other necessary household expenditure was calculated after careful investigation on a similarly economical basis. Further, it was assumed that every penny earned by every member of the family went into the family purse.

The cost (exclusive of rent) at 1936 prices of maintaining families of different sizes on this level is shown in the following table . . .

Family	Food		Sundries		Total	
	s.	d.	s.	d.	s.	d.
1 man (working)	4	11	6	1	11	0
1 woman (working)	4	3	5	8	9	11
1 man, 1 woman	9	2	7	2	16	4
1 man, 1 woman, 1 child	12	7	8	2	20	9
1 man, 1 woman, 2 children	16	0	9	2	25	2
1 man, 1 woman, 3 children	19	5	11	2	30	7
1 man, 1 woman, 4 children	22	10	12	2	35	0

Plus 3s. 5d. for food, and 1s. for all else for each additional child.

As elsewhere in this volume, the actual rent paid has in every case been assumed to represent the minimum necessary rent expenditure. Save in exceptional circumstances, those in abject poverty do not spend more on rent than they need.

I can best give a picture of what life at the primary poverty level means by quoting from my previous volume.

A family living upon the scale allowed for in this estimate must never spend a penny on railway fare or omnibus. They must never go into the country unless they walk. They must never purchase a half-penny newspaper or spend a penny to buy a ticket for a popular concert. They must write no letters to absent children, for they cannot afford to pay the postage. They must never contribute anything to their church or chapel, or give any help to a neighbour which costs them money. They cannot save, nor can they join sick clubs or trade unions, because they cannot pay the necessary subscriptions. The children must have no pocket money for dolls, marbles or sweets. The father must smoke no tobacco, and must drink no beer. The mother must never buy any pretty clothes for herself or for her children, the character of the family wardrobe, as for the family diet, being governed by the regulation, 'Nothing must be bought but what is absolutely necessary for the maintenance of physical health, and what is bought must be of the plainest and most economical description.' Should a child fall ill, it must be attended by the parish doctor; should it die, it must be buried by the parish.

Finally, the wage-earner must never be absent from his work for a single day.

B.S. Rowntree, *Poverty and Progress*, 1941, pp. 28–9, 103–4.

Questions

1. *Describe how Rowntree calculates his poverty line.*
2. *What assumptions does he make about the control that families, and housewives in particular, have over their life-style and spending patterns?*
3. *In what ways is Rowntree's concept of a poverty line similar to the concept of health implied in the medical model?*

A second and more recent model defines poverty in terms of social deprivation rather than physical subsistence. Like the social model of health, it incorporates the insider's rather than the outsider's perspective on poverty. It does not define poverty in absolute money terms, but in the context of the standards of living enjoyed by the majority of the population. Poverty, it suggests, cannot be understood in isolation, but only relative to the existence of wealth. The model encompasses material deprivation but also links poverty to the idea of powerlessness and stigma. The poor are those who lack the power to control their destiny. They are thus the objects of state surveillance, supervised by social security officials and social workers. They experience poverty as a stigma, a condition they see the welfare state as mediating and reinforcing.

Reading 6

Often in academic discussion about welfare a distinction is made between the absolute and relative concepts of poverty. On an absolute criterion the poor are those who have insufficient resources to achieve some fixed standard of living. In the 1930s in Britain there was a good deal of research undertaken to establish basic minima of diet, clothing etc. below which physiological efficiency could not be sustained. It is now generally accepted that absolute definitions of poverty, however 'scientific' the appearance they present, are simply irrelevant to social realities. People's lives revolve round the social relationships in which they are involved. The complex deprivations summarized in the term *poverty* cannot begin to be measured in terms of the calories in a daily diet. Only some kind of relative conception of poverty is in any way illuminating. Poverty is an inability to achieve a standard of living allowing for self-respect, the respect of others, and for full participation in society.

In the last analysis, to be poor is not just to be located at the tail end of some distribution of income, but to be placed in a particular relationship of inferiority to the wider society. Poverty involves a particular sort of powerlessness, an inability to control the circumstances of one's life in the face of more powerful groups in society. All this, however, should not be taken as an argument that money is irrelevant, either to the social problem of poverty, or to the problems of the poor. One of the most prevalent and comforting of middle-class doctrines about the nature of poverty is that it is not lack of money, but inability to manage what resources one has, which is the root cause of poverty . . . Yet it is the existence of such attitudes, allied to the social power to translate them into organizations for 'dealing' with the problem of poverty, which gives an essential clue to the meaning of the experience of being poor. It is to be dependent for needed assistance on social agencies which have the power to investigate your personal life, can involve you in bureaucratic complications, and can stigmatize you as immoral or inadequate according to *their* standards. Sometimes you may be helpfully and courteously treated by the officer from the Ministry or the social worker or the hospital receptionist. But in any case, how you are treated is very largely out of your control. The arbitrariness of circumstance is a dominant theme in the experience of poverty.

J. Kincaid, *Poverty and Inequality in Britain*, 1973, pp. 158–9.

Questions
1. *On what grounds does Kincaid reject an absolute model of poverty?*
2. *Identify the key elements in the alternative model outlined by the author.*
3. *In what ways is Kincaid's perspective on poverty similar to the social model of health?*

The final reading in this chapter deals with the measurement problems inherent in an absolute model of poverty. Peter Townsend argues that the idea of a fixed subsistence standard (or poverty line) is central both to social research on poverty and to the management of the social security system which provides a basic level of income to those in need. He takes issue with the

way in which the standard is measured in both these areas. In
particular, he argues that despite the apparent objectivity of the
concept of a poverty line, it masks personal and moral
judgements. It is not a value-neutral concept, but one which
reflects a particular and middle-class view on the needs of the
working-class family.

Reading 7

One of the basic aims of social policy in the years immediately
following the [second world] war was the elimination of poverty.
In order to find how far this aim has been realised there must be
adequate inquiries from time to time in the form of social surveys
which adopt certain definite standards of measurement . . .

The standard selected is important not only to the research
worker intent on measuring the extent of poverty or general
living conditions in any locality. A standard of a similar kind has
been used in framing social policy. Social security benefit
payments are intended to be related to a rough standard of
subsistence . . .

The sociological study and measurement of poverty in this
century dates from the pioneering work of Charles Booth and B.
Seebohm Rowntree at the end of the last century . . . The
studies that followed in the next forty years adopted the same
approach and although there were some minor alterations, the
standards used for measuring poverty were broadly the same,
adjusted according to change in prices, as that used by Rowntree
in 1899 . . .

The main fault in the standards used has been their lack of
relation to the budgets and customs of life of working people.
Many who are considered to be above the poverty line because
their income exceeds the total cost of meeting basic needs do, in
fact, spend less on the individual items included in the standard –
food, clothing, fuel and light and household sundries – simply
because they spend money on other things . . . How those on the
borderline of poverty ought to spend their money is a very
different thing from how they do spend their money. It would be
unrealistic to expect them, as in effect many social investigators
have expected them, to be skilled dieticians with marked
tendencies towards puritanism.

In all the definitions of poverty in the social surveys there is the
implication that many poor people ought to limit their spending

to a short list of 'necessaries' laid down by those in charge of the surveys and that if they did not do this they were in poverty only through their own fault. 'Our definition is such that a family is deemed to be in poverty if the joint income of the members, *supposing it were all available and wisely spent*, would not suffice to purchase for them the necessaries of life . . .' (p. 148, *Social Survey of Merseyside*, my italics) . . . It was not appreciated that many in the working class would have needed virtues of self-denial, skill and knowledge not possessed by any other class of society, if they were to spend their money as it was thought they should spend it.

Judgments of one social class on another are notoriously untrustworthy and things which are treated as necessaries by one group may not be so regarded by another . . . Recent experience of the effects of unemployment in the cotton towns in Lancashire showed that when incomes were reduced from a full wage to an unemployment insurance allowance many families were apt to cut down on things such as meat and fruit in order not to forgo an occasional visit to a cinema or football match . . .

The pattern of spending among poor people is largely determined by the accepted modes of behaviour in the communities in which they live, and these, in turn, are determined to some extent by the practices adopted by the society as a whole through central and local government. A yardstick for measuring poverty can only be devised in the light of knowledge about family budgets . . .

[This argument] has an important bearing on the standards adopted in social policy for benefit payments. Lord Beveridge, in his *Report on Social Insurance and Allied Services*, formulated a subsistence standard very similar to the poverty lines used in the social surveys before the war, as a reasonable way of fixing benefit rates. This was generally regarded as the 'central idea' of the Beveridge Plan . . . The National Assistance scales (and today's rates of Supplementary Benefit) are determined by means of a similar standard . . . and neither the Labour nor the Conservative Party has explicitly abandoned this principle.

Whether in fact the subsistence basis for benefit payments should be accepted by the nation in the future is one of the fundamental questions that will have to be faced by Parliament . . . The acceptance of a standard such as the pre-war poverty line or the Beveridge subsistence minimum implies that poor working-class people should and could live as social scientists and administrators think they should live. There has been little attempt to discuss the distinction between 'luxuries' and 'necessities' in terms of economic and social sanctions for spending behaviour, nor in terms of individual and class differences. And there has been no attempt to distinguish between the humanly attainable and the desirable in the pattern of family budgets.

> P. Townsend, 'Measuring poverty', *British Journal of Sociology*, 1954, pp. 130, 132–3, 135–6.

Questions

1. *What are Townsend's main criticisms of the idea of a subsistence standard?*
2. *Do you accept his view that the acceptance of Rowntree's subsistence standard 'implies that poor working-class people should and could live as social scientists and administrators think they should live'?*
3. *What kind of measure of poverty would overcome Townsend's criticisms?*
4. *Using material from readings 5, 6 and 7, re-read the terms listed on page 14 (reading 4, question 4). How many of the pairs of terms can be applied to the subsistence and social models of welfare?*

ESSAY QUESTIONS

1. 'From a sociological point of view, there is no objective definition of illness, instead it is necessary to ask in whose interest, and with what purpose in mind, illness is socially defined by different people.' Drawing on examples, explain the meaning of this statement and show how states of illness are socially defined. (JMB, 1980)
2. Examine the problems that sociologists face in defining and measuring poverty. (AEB, 1982)
3. What problems are encountered in defining and measuring poverty? How have sociologists attempted to overcome these problems of definition and measurement? (Oxford Local Examinations, 1983)
4. 'Whether or not a person is defined and treated as ill will depend in part on a series of negotiations between that person and the doctor.' Using examples, explain the meaning of this statement. To what extent is it acceptable to claim that it is doctors and patients who decide what is illness and what is health? (JMB, 1982)
5. 'Social statistics are really social products.' Consider the full significance of this observation in relation to *one* area of sociological enquiry. (University of London, 1982)

FURTHER READING

1. P. Townsend and N. Davidson, *Inequalities in Health*, Penguin, 1982, pp. 41–50.
   Discusses the problems of defining and measuring the concepts of health and inequality.

2. K. Coates and R. Silburn, *Poverty: The Forgotten Englishmen*, Penguin, 1981, pp. 33–50.
   Examines the problem of defining poverty and how different researchers have solved it.

3. New Society Social Studies Reader, *How the Poorest Live*, New Society, 1982, articles by P. Harrison on 'Making ends meet' and 'The poorest: their homes'.
   Describes the reality of living in poverty.

4. B. Ehrenreich and D. English, *Complaints and Disorders: The Sexual Politics of Sickness*, Writers and Readers Publishing Co-operative, 1973, pp. 19–48.
   Describes how the frail and sickly image of upper-class women developed in the nineteenth century, and the role of medicine in sustaining it.

5. D. Tuckett and J. Kaufert (eds), *Basic Readings in Medical Sociology*, Tavistock, 1978, articles by G. Stimson and B. Webb on 'The face-to-face interaction and after the consultation' and I. Zola on 'Medicine as an institution of social control'.
   The first article describes how patients feel about and try to influence what happens during a consultation with their doctor. The second article looks at how medicine and medical ways of thinking are taking over increasing areas of everyday life.

2
Explaining poverty and ill-health

INTRODUCTION

Definitions of poverty and ill-health tend to be closely linked to explanations of how these conditions are caused. This chapter examines some of the explanations aligned with the social and individual definitions identified in Chapter 1.

Explaining poverty and ill-health involves explaining differences in the economic circumstances and life-experiences of individuals in society. These differences are not randomly distributed; there are systematic patterns in the statistics on income and mortality which suggest that certain groups are significantly more vulnerable than others.

The distribution of wealth and health closely follows the contours of Britain's social structure. Wealth and health, for example, are both closely related to sexual and racial divisions. For women living alone, poverty and the death of their children are more common experiences than for married women; they are more common, too, among black than white parents. Patterns of wealth and health similarly highlight the existence of class differences in living standards and life chances. Families in social class five have weekly incomes one third of those in social class one (OPCS, 1982, *General Household Survey*, Table 2.13). Their health is correspondingly worse. Children born into social class five are more than twice as likely to die in the first year of life as those born into social class one. 'Social class' here is defined in terms of a status-grading of occupations (doctors above secretaries, secretaries above factory-workers). While accepting that such a definition is useful in highlighting the influence of social structure on individual welfare, many sociologists are unhappy about this concept of class. They argue that social class is not a 'thing', like a job, but a relationship between groups of people who occupy different and unequal positions within society. The existence of a social class structure in Britain, they suggest, does not so much signify a consensus about the relative worth of different occupations but rather a deep-rooted struggle for power and control over the economy.

Understanding the nature of social class (and gender and race) is important if sociologists are to unravel the cause of illness and

24

poverty. Their explanations should not only tell us why some *individuals* are poor and ill; in addition, their theories have to explain why certain *groups* of individuals are especially vulnerable to hardship. Their theories must explain why social class, gender, age, race and area of residence all appear to have such a pervasive impact on poverty and ill-health. Thus explanations of poverty and illness inevitably have built into them certain (often veiled) assumptions about the nature of Britain's social structure – its class structure, and its system of gender and racial divisions.

Two sets of causes emerge in the explanatory models which social scientists have developed. Some social scientists explain poverty and ill-health in terms of the characteristics of the poor themselves. An enduring theme in these explanations is that the problems besetting the poor and the unhealthy lie in their biology, personality or culture. The victims of poverty and ill-health are themselves the primary cause of their suffering. Other social scientists explain this suffering in terms of social and economic forces beyond the individual. A recurring theme in these perspectives is that individual differences in income and health are caused by social inequalities, which are deeply woven into the fabric of society. In this chapter, the two kinds of explanation are identified as victim-blaming theories and system-blaming theories.

In explaining present-day patterns of ill-health and poverty, sociologists often look to the past, to see if historical evidence can shed light on current trends. They have turned particularly to the historical research of Thomas McKeown, which sought to explain the fall in mortality from infectious diseases during the nineteenth century. Although medicine was growing rapidly at the time that mortality was falling, McKeown argues that the expansion of medicine was not the cause of the improvement in the nation's health. Instead, he points to improvements in living conditions and the fall in the birthrate. His conclusions are contained in the first reading below. They help provide a historical perspective offering insights which may be missing in the sociological explanations considered in the sections below.

Reading 1

The period from about the beginning of the eighteenth century to the present day was one of change from an agricultural to an industrial way of life . . . In developed countries there have been profound changes in economic conditions, from poverty to affluence, and in the character of the common disease problems, from infectious to non-communicable diseases . . . The first and most important reason for the decline of infectious diseases was an improvement in nutrition. It resulted from advances in agriculture which spread through the western world from about the end of the seventeenth century . . . Second only to nutritional influences, in time and probably in importance, were the improvements in hygiene introduced progressively from the second half of the nineteenth century . . . In the nineteenth century there were no large improvements in working and living conditions and the main advances were in purification of water and sewage disposal. From about 1900 these measures were greatly extended by food hygiene, affecting most critically the quality of milk . . . The rapid fall of deaths from gastro-enteritis, which contributed substantially to the decline in infant mortality, was due to the introduction of sterilisation, bottling and safe transport of milk. Environmental measures have, of course, been extended in the present century, by improvements in working and living conditions, taking the latter to include advances (such as control of atmospheric pollution) in the community as well as in domestic circumstances . . .

The other reason for the modern transformation of health was the change in reproductive behaviour which led to the decline of the birth rate . . . While the initial progress was due to other influences, the change in reproductive practices which restricted numbers was the essential complement without which the advances would soon have been reversed.

T. McKeown, *The Role of Medicine*, 1979, pp. 76–7.

Questions
1. *What factors does McKeown identify as responsible for the decline of infectious diseases in the Western world over the last 200 years?*
2. *McKeown is describing the pattern of disease in early industrial Britain. What conclusions, if any, can be drawn for the Third World, where infectious diseases are still major killers?*
3. *What conclusions, if any, can be drawn for the control of the non-infectious and disabling diseases which are the major killers today in the Western world?*

VICTIM-BLAMING THEORIES

Victim-blaming theories have a long history, with their heyday in the period of rapid industrialisation between the mid-seventeenth and early twentieth centuries. Significantly, as Britain again experiences rapid economic change, these theories are becoming popular once more. Fundamental to this perspective is an absolute conception of human welfare. Poverty means living on an income insufficient for survival; ill-health means having a disorder which can be diagnosed and understood without reference to the wider society. Except in a small minority of cases, poverty and ill-health are seen as avoidable. In nineteenth-century Britain, it was the received wisdom that both were the result of the failure of individuals to prepare themselves adequately for the responsibilities of work and family life. Economists of the time, like Adam Smith, maintained that the economy provided work, at some wage, for everyone. The poor were therefore poor because they avoided work or misspent the money they earned. According to the Charity Organisation Society, the main body coordinating professional social work at the end of the nineteenth century:

> There can be no doubt that the poverty of the working class of England is due, not to their circumstances (which are more favourable than those of any other working population in Europe); but to their improvident habits and thriftlessness. If they are ever to be more prosperous it must be through self-denial, temperance and forethought (1881, Vol. 10, p. 50, cited in Jones, *State Social Work and the Working Class*, p. 76).

The existence of large numbers living in poverty indicated only that there were large numbers of work-shy and improvident people among the working class. As one eighteenth-century observer wrote, 'everyone but an idiot knows that the lower class must be kept poor or they will never be industrious' (quoted in Tawney, *Religion and the Rise of Capitalism*, p. 268).

Like poverty, ill-health was regarded as a disease which could be corrected through improvements in the character and personal habits of the individual. Women, as the caretakers of family health, were heavily implicated in the spread of ill-health. It was their ignorance and lack of training which was blamed for the squalid conditions in which the poor lived. The standards of home-making were linked particularly to infant mortality, which, in 1904, stood at 145 deaths per 1000 live births. (Today it is 12 per 1000.) A representative voice was that of George Newman, the first Chief Medical Officer at the Board of Education from 1907 and an influential figure in the movement to improve child health. His views are summarised in the first part of Reading 2.

Victim-blaming explanations of poverty and ill-health, dominant until the turn of the century, have waned but never died. The multinational survey by the European Economic Community of *Perceptions of Poverty* (Commission of the European Community, 1977), shows that 'laziness and lack of will power' were the most widely-believed causes of poverty in Britain, a much more popular explanation than in other countries. Current Conservative philo-sophy accords with this popular theory of poverty. While acknowledging that the recession has its innocent casualties, it argues that there are other groups for whom unemployment and poverty are self-inflicted.

Similarly, within the field of health, certain types of ill-health are again being explained as a failure of will-power and discipline. The major infectious diseases are no longer the killers they once were and the control of the modern epidemics of coronary heart disease and cancer is seen to lie primarily with the individual. The second part of Reading 2, drawn from the White Paper, *Prevention and Health*, published in 1977, illustrates the way in which victim-blaming theories are applied today.

Reading 2

The problem of infant mortality is not one of sanitation alone, or housing or, indeed, of poverty as such, but is mainly a question of motherhood . . . death in infancy is probably more due to such ignorance and negligence than to almost any other cause, as becomes evident when we remember that epidemic diarrhoea, convulsive debility and atrophy which are among the most common causes of death, are brought about in large measure owing to improper feeding or ill-timed weaning; bronchitis and pneumonia are due not infrequently to careless exposure (indoor or outdoor); and death from measles and whooping cough is largely caused by mismanagement of nursing. To remedy this condition of things, three measures are needed to be carried out: (a) instruction of mothers; (b) the appointment of lady health visitors and (c) the education of girls in domestic hygiene.

G. Newman, *Infant Mortality: A Social Problem*, 1906, pp. 257, 262.

Much ill-health in Britain today arises from over-indulgence and unwise behaviour. Not surprisingly, the greatest potential and perhaps the greatest problem for preventive medicine now lies in changing behaviour and attitudes of health. The individual can do much to help himself, his family and the community by accepting more personal responsibility for his own health and well-being . . .

Department of Health and Social Security, *Prevention and Health*, 1977, p. 39.

Questions

1. *What factors are identified by Newman as the causes of infant mortality?*
2. *In what ways could his explanation be described as victim-blaming?*

3. *What kinds of behaviour do you think the authors of* Prevention and Health *have in mind when they speak of 'over-indulgence and unwise behaviour'?*

4. *Do you think that the way in which the authors of* Prevention and Health *explain ill-health is victim-blaming?*

While political and public sympathies may favour victim-blaming theories, there are few contemporary social scientists who would argue that laziness and self-indulgence are the main causes of poverty and ill-health. However, this does not mean that they all accept that hardship and suffering is created through the structure of society. While rejecting that poverty and illness are a mark of personal inadequacy, some argue that it is caused by the values that the poor hold and pass onto their children. These values, and the life-style they sustain, are seen as different to those found in the rest of society. It is these values which are held to blame for the perpetuation of poverty and ill-health 'in the midst of plenty'.

Reflecting its emphasis on culture and socialisation, this perspective is variously referred to as 'the culture of poverty' and 'the transmitted deprivation hypothesis'. In some accounts, recognition is given to the structural position of the poor, marginal to the labour market and confined to low-paid work and recurrent periods of unemployment. However, the emphasis tends to be upon values and attitudes rather than on economic processes. It is this emphasis that Sir Keith Joseph captured in his speech on transmitted deprivation, given in 1972 when he was Secretary of State for Social Services. He commented how 'inadequate people tend to be inadequate parents and inadequate parents tend to rear inadequate children' (his speech is published in Butterworth and Holman, *Social Welfare in Modern Britain*, 1975).

The major sociological exponent of the culture of poverty model is Oscar Lewis, who, in a series of books, recorded the quality of life among the poor of Mexico and Central America. The extract below is taken from one of these books.

Reading 3

The culture of poverty is both an adaptation and a reaction of the poor to their marginal position in a class-stratified, highly individuated, capitalistic society. It represents an effort to cope with feelings of hopelessness and despair which develop from the realisation of the improbability of achieving success in terms of the values and goals of the larger society . . .

The culture of poverty, however, is not only an adaptation to a set of objective conditions of the larger society. Once it comes into existence it tends to perpetuate itself from generation to generation because of its effect on the children. By the time slum children are age six or seven they have usually absorbed the basic values and attitudes of their subculture and are not psychologically geared to take full advantage of changing conditions or increased opportunities which may occur in their lifetime . . .

The lack of effective participation and integration of the poor in the major institutions of the larger society is one of the crucial characteristics of the culture of poverty . . . People with a culture of poverty produce very little wealth and receive very little in return. They have a low level of literacy and education, usually do not belong to labor unions, are not members of political parties, generally do not participate in the national welfare agencies, and make very little use of banks, hospitals, department stores, museums or art galleries. They have a critical attitude toward some of the basic institutions of the dominant classes, hatred of the police, mistrust of government and those in high position, and a cynicism which extends even to the church. This gives the culture of poverty a high potential for protest and for being used in political movements aimed against the existing social order . . . When we look at the culture of poverty on the local community level, we find poor housing conditions, crowding, gregariousness, but above all a minimum of organization beyond the level of the nuclear and extended family.

Occasionally there are informal, temporary groupings or voluntary associations within slums. The existence of neighborhood gangs which cut across slum settlements represents a considerable advance beyond the zero point of the continuum that I have in mind. Indeed, it is the low level of organization which gives the culture of poverty its marginal and anachronistic quality in our highly complex, specialized, organized society. Most primitive peoples have achieved a higher level of sociocultural organization than our modern urban slum dwellers . . .

On the level of the individual the major characteristics are a strong feeling of marginality, of helplessness, of dependence and of inferiority . . .

Other traits include a high incidence of maternal deprivation, of orality, of weak ego structure, confusion of sexual identification, a lack of impulse control, a strong present-time orientation with relatively little ability to defer gratification and to plan for the future, a sense of resignation and fatalism, a widespread belief in male superiority, and a high tolerance for psychological pathology of all sorts.

People with a culture of poverty are provincial and locally oriented and have very little sense of history. They know only their own troubles, their own local conditions, their own neighborhood, their own way of life. Usually they do not have the knowledge, the vision or the ideology to see the similarities between their problems and those of their counterparts elsewhere in the world.

> O. Lewis, *La Vida: A Puerto Rican Family in the Culture of Poverty – San Juan and New York*, 1965, pp. xli–xliv.

Questions
1. *What does Lewis mean by the statement that the culture of poverty is both 'an adaptation and a reaction of the poor'?*
2. *What are 'the basic values and attitudes' of the subculture that slum children absorb?*
3. *In what ways can the culture of poverty be identified as a victim-blaming model?*
4. *Is there any evidence to suggest, from Lewis's account, that 'the culture of poverty' is not a value-neutral concept?*

Critics of such explanations of poverty and ill-health argue that terms like 'cultural deprivation' are simply white, middle-class prejudice in a scientific disguise. 'Deprivation', they claim, is used not in a material but a moral sense. According to Neil Keddie, 'cultural deprivation' is 'a euphemism for saying that working-class and ethnic groups have cultures which are at least dissonant with, if not inferior to, the "mainstream" culture of the society at large' (Keddie, *Tinker, Tailor . . . The Myth of Cultural Deprivation*, p. 7). It is a euphemism, moreover, which 'individualises failure' by identifying problems in the home environment and not in the nature and organisation of society.

SYSTEM-BLAMING THEORIES

Like victim-blaming theories, the doctrine of social causes has a long history. However, social scientists, politicians and welfare professionals have traditionally been reluctant to give the doctrine much house-room. Today, as in the nineteenth century, it is identified as an 'anti-establishment' position, espoused by those who are marginal to the mainstream of political and academic life. Part of the reason lies in its searing criticisms of modern society, the disquieting picture it paints of an underworld of inequality and oppression beneath an affluent facade. Part of the reason lies in its radical prescriptions for change; its argument for a major restructuring of the labour market and a major equalising of incomes and life-chances across the social divides of class, race and sex. Part of the reason lies in the fact that, seen from within the established victim-blaming paradigm, the system-blaming doctrine is profoundly wrong.

Fundamental to the system-blaming perspective is a relative conception of poverty and a social conception of health. Since poverty is relative, it cannot be understood by focusing on the poor alone. Rather, poverty can only be understood in the context of wealth; in the context of a society organised around economic differences between people. In the rigidly-stratified society of feudal England, poverty was regarded as a natural and unalterable fact of life for serfs, with wealth the proper condition for lords. In the same way, the social hierarchies of modern society are seen to create poor and rich. In modern society, however, it is the social divisions associated not with feudalism but with the rise of capitalism which structure the nature and distribution of poverty. These social divisions are seen to create a condition of economic dependency for large sections of the population. Placed outside or on the margins of the labour market, they find themselves dependent on the state and on their families for survival.

Fuelling the creation of poverty and dependency is seen to be the organisation of waged work. Particular attention is drawn to the separation of the employed from the unemployed and, within the labour market, the existence of a primary sector of 'good jobs' which are secure, well-paid and satisfying and a secondary sector where jobs are insecure, poorly paid and repetitive. The poor are those who find themselves restricted to the shrinking secondary sector of employment.

Such divisions within the labour market are seen as closely related to divisions outside it. Racial divisions ensure that black workers are disproportionately represented in the twilight areas of the economy. Sexual divisions, too, are involved in the creation of dependency. Much of women's work is done 'for love' outside the labour market, and their paid employment is largely restricted to low-paying jobs which are the market equivalent of the work they do at home for nothing: making food and clothing, cleaning and catering, nursing and teaching (Equal Opportunities Commission, *Seventh Annual Report: 1982*, 1983).

These social divisions, and the inequalities of wealth which they sustain, are seen to provide the explanation of ill-health as well as poverty. In fact, ill-health is seen as a by-product of poverty and economic dependency; a measure of the cumulative effect that material deprivation can have on the human body. This materialist or structural explanation traces the causes of ill-health to the social structure which governs the distribution of such material resources as housing, food, warmth and safe working conditions for adults and safe play-spaces for children. It is this kind of explanation which the recently-appointed Working Group on *Inequalities in Health* found the most convincing. They conclude, from their review of the evidence that

> choosing between such complex and sometimes competing approaches, when applied to evidence as complex as that which we have assembled, is a daunting task. We must make clear our belief that it is in some form or forms of the 'materialist' approach that the best answer lies. But there can be little doubt that amongst all the evidence there is much that is convincingly explained in alternative terms: cultural, social selection and so on (Townsend and Davidson, *Inequalities in Health*, 1982, pp. 122–3).

In explaining how material conditions determine health, they focus on different stages of the life-cycle. Looking at the causes of illness and death in infancy, they suggest the concrete ways in which wealth is translated into health.

Reading 4

. . . Any factors which increase the parental capacity to provide adequate care for an infant will, when present, increase the chance of survival, while their absence will increase the risk of premature death. The most obvious of such factors fall within the sphere of material resources: sufficient household income, a safe, uncrowded and unpolluted home, warmth and hygiene, a means of rapid communication with the outside world, for example a telephone or car, and an adequate level of manpower – or womanpower (two parents would normally provide more continuous care and protection than one). In addition to these basic material needs must be added other cognitive and motivational factors which are not independent of the distribution of material advantage. Those factors would include knowledge, certain skills and resources in verbal communication and a high level of motivation to provide continuous and loving care. When all these factors are present the infant's chance of survival is very good indeed. When some or even many of these are absent, the outlook is less propitious. Moreover, it should not be forgotten that these very same factors play a part in determining the development of the infant's own cognitive/linguistic and other skills. Competence acquired at this stage of life can profoundly influence later intellectual (and hence educational) achievement.

P. Townsend and N. Davidson, *Inequalities in Health*, 1982, pp. 124–5.

Questions

1. *What do Townsend and Davidson identify as the causes of class inequality in health?*
2. *How might George Newman (Reading 2) respond to their analysis?*
3. *What are the main differences between Townsend and Davidson's materialist model and the culture of poverty model developed by Lewis (Reading 3)?*

The materialist explanation may not sound altogether dissimilar to the culture of poverty perspective, discussed in the previous section. The difference lies in the identification of root causes. The cultural explanation identifies values as the primary causal agents in health; it is they which prevent the individual acquiring the knowledge and habits necessary for good health. The Working Group, while accepting that psychology and culture have their part to play, argue that it is primarily lack of money, and the resources it buys, which prevents many people achieving a life-style which promotes their health.

Some versions of this system-blaming perspective take their analysis of the social structure further. These models, discussed in Chapters 3 and 5, argue that the welfare state and the welfare professions serve to perpetuate the patterns of poverty and ill-health. The models thus identify as a major cause of hardship and suffering the institutions which claim to alleviate them. This kind of explanation draws attention to the fact that poverty and ill-health are shaped by ideologies as well as by material conditions. Once patterns of poverty and ill-health are established, they can serve to reinforce popular beliefs which block the introduction of the radical social policies necessary to eliminate inequality. Robert Holman has suggested that the visible existence of poverty serves an ideological role in encouraging the work-ethic in others and supporting the view that the poor have only themselves to blame. Publicity on ill-health, too, can be similarly seen as a timely reminder of how much illness is self-induced and could be avoided through a firm commitment to 'look after yourself'.

Reading 5

The existence, even the creation, of a group identified as the poor serves to set them apart from the rest of the population. The result is not just . . . that the working class is divided and thereby weakened. Rather, the use of the poor as a reference group persuades those sections of society (which are neither wealthy nor poor) that their lot in terms of status, resources and power is acceptable. Consequently, the possibility that they will strive to change the position of the elite is reduced. Further, they (the poor) act as a warning. They demonstrate the fate of those who do not conform to prevailing work and social standards. Their plight is needed to reinforce the will of others to work for low returns in unpleasant and even degrading conditions from which the economic output gives a disproportionate financial reward to a minority of existing resource holders. Not least, those in poverty act as scapegoats, a vulnerable group on whom the blame for social problems can be placed, so diverting attention away from that minority which has some control over social affairs.

R. Holman, 'Another model of poverty' in E. Butterworth and R. Holman, *Social Welfare in Modern Britain*, 1975, p. 411.

Questions

1. *In Holman's account, in what ways does the existence of poverty help perpetuate social divisions?*
2. *What evidence can you think of which challenges or supports Holman's argument?*
3. *What does Holman mean by the statement that the existence of the poor 'divides' and 'weakens' the working class?*

System-blaming theories, like victim-blaming theories, have not gone unchallenged. There are two main lines of criticism. First, it is argued that our scientific measures of health, poverty, social class and ethnicity are only approximations of a complex reality. Statistical relationships found between these indicators (between social class and health, for example) may not exist in the real world. Our theories may therefore rest on the artificial picture conjured up by the crude indicators that we use. Another and more powerful criticism of the materialist explanation rests on a theory of natural or social selection. This theory (supported, in part, by the work of Jon Stern) recognises a real relationship between health, poverty and social class but argues that cause and effect have been wrongly identified. It is not poverty which creates ill-health, but ill-health which creates poverty. In this model, while the healthy go up in the class hierarchy, so that mortality rates among the higher social classes are kept low, the unhealthy go down in the class hierarchy, inflating the rates of death and disability among social classes four and five.

Disentangling social class from personal health is a complex process, yet it is crucial for this model that we can distinguish 'natural health' from the cumulative impact of inequality on those at the bottom of the occupational hierarchy. Establishing the extent of social mobility is also a necessary part of the theory. For the model to work, healthy individuals must be able to move up the social hierarchy and become rich, while unhealthy individuals fall into poverty. Evidence suggests that while many people do move a small way up or down the social class ladder during their lives, the extent of social mobility is not sufficient to account for the observed class differences in mortality. As yet, sociologists have debated this model of natural selection only rarely. But it is one likely to make an increasing impact on the controversy about poverty and ill-health. Its basic view of society is similar to the one found within the Victorian victim-blaming paradigm, with the class structure seen as an expression of moral worth (Hart, 'Understanding debates about health inequality', 1983). Wealth and upper class status are the rewards which ensure that the most talented and energetic people are recruited to the most important posts in industry, commerce and government. Poverty, and life-long relegation to the working class, are the inevitable consequence for the less talented and resourceful majority.

Both victim-blaming and system-blaming theories provide explanations of the life-experiences of individuals and groups. Some sociologists regard these explanations as complimentary: they suggest that we need both to understand health and welfare. Others argue the two positions offer competing rather than complimentary analyses. In fact, historically, victim-blaming and system-blaming theories have become aligned to the right and left of Britain's political spectrum, making reconciliation in practice difficult to achieve. Today, the two models are closely linked to two distinct policy agendas. These both seek, in very different ways, to make radical changes in society which would limit the extent of poverty and ill-health to its unavoidable minimum.

The complex ways in which victim-blaming and system-blaming perspectives are linked to questions of politics and policy-making will become clearer in later chapters.

ESSAY QUESTIONS

1. Examine the tables below and answer the questions which follow.

Table 1. Life Expectancy at Birth for Males in England and Wales

Year of Birth	1931	1951	1961	1971
Life expectancy in years	58.4	66.4	67.9	69.3

Table 2. *Death Rates for Males (aged 15–64) in Different Social Classes in England and Wales. The death rates are expressed as percentages above and below average (the average for the total population in the age range would, therefore, be expressed as 0% in this table).*

	1931 %	1951 %	1961 %	1971 %
Social Classes I & II	−7	−10	−20	−20
Social Classes IV & V	+7	+10	+15	+20

   (a) Briefly describe what the two tables show about the pattern of male life expectation over the last fifty years.

   (b) What factors might account for what is shown in the tables? (JMB, 1979)

2. Critically review explanations of social problems that focus on (i) the inadequacy of individuals and (ii) their social situations. Briefly outline the policy implications of such explanations. (JMB, 1981)

3. Critically examine the usefulness of the idea of 'cycles of deprivation' in explaining the persistence of poverty. (JMB, 1979)

4. 'People cannot be culturally deprived, only culturally different.' Discuss and illustrate. (University of London, 1982)

5. 'Social inequality is always accompanied by a set of beliefs that claim that those who are poor or powerless deserve to be so.' Discuss in relation to *two* or more forms of social inequality. (University of London, 1982)

6. Account for differences in mortality rates between social classes since 1900. (Oxford Local Examinations, 1983)

7. Examine the following leaflet advertising a tenants' association meeting and read the accompanying paragraph. Then answer the questions which follow.

> Condensation and damp may seem to be minor problems but throughout the country people in areas where poverty, disadvantages and various other social problems are prevalent, have discovered that what they saw as personal problems are common and cannot be put down simply to personal inadequacies. They have drawn attention to the conditions in which they live and have come together in an attempt to improve the quality of their lives and to increase the resources available to them. They have formed community action groups such as tenants' associations and claimants' unions; these and similar groups have become much more common in the past two decades.

   (a) What assumptions concerning the nature of social problems might lie behind the council officer's statement in the cartoon?

   (b) Give *two* examples of the policy implications which might stem from such assumptions concerning the nature of any *one* social problem which you have studied. (JMB, 1982)

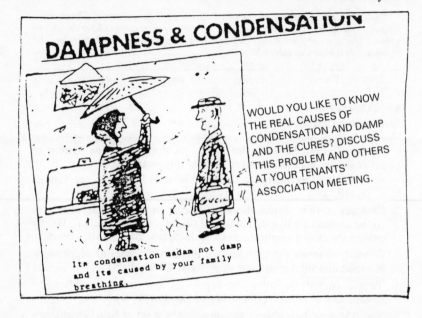

FURTHER READING

1. K. Coates and R. Silburn, *Poverty: The Forgotten Englishmen*, Penguin, 1981, pp. 148–67.

   Describes the concepts of deprivation and the culture of poverty and examines the evidence on the lives of the poor in Nottingham to see whether the concepts explain their attitudes and living conditions.

2. New Society Social Sciences Reader, *How The Poorest Live*, New Society, 1982, articles by P. Golding and J. Middleton 'Why is the press so obsessed with welfare scroungers?' and P. Golding 'It's the poor what gets the blame'.

   The first article examines the origins and effects of 'scrounger phobia', looking at images of claimants in the national dailies in the mid-1970s. The second article looks more deeply into social beliefs about poverty and the poor, highlighting the widespread belief that the poor are the cause of poverty.

3. R. Berthoud, 'Transmitted deprivation: the kite that failed', *Policy Studies*, 1983, 3, 3, pp. 151–69.

   Describes the origins and outcome of a major piece of social research to establish whether a cycle of deprivation explained the persistence of poverty and ill-health.

4. L. Doyal, *The Political Economy of Health*, Pluto Press, 1979, pp. 49–95 and pp. 96–138.

   Describes the class patterns of health over the last 100 years, in both

Britain and the Third World, and develops a materialist, system-blaming model to explain them.

5. R. Holman, *Poverty: Explanations of Social Deprivation*, Martin Robertson, 1978, pp. 54–68, 86–104, 105–46.

Examines various influential theories of poverty which see genetic factors, problem families and the culture of poverty as responsible for the persistence of inequality.

6. A. Coote, 'Inequalities in health' in M. O'Donnell (ed), *New Introductory Reader in Sociology*, Harrap, pp. 445–50.

A review of the Department of Health and Social Security's enquiry into class inequalities in health published by Townsend and Davidson as *Inequalities in Health*, Penguin, 1982.

7. S. MacPherson, *Social Policy in the Third World*, Wheatsheaf Books, 1982, pp. 15–83, 93–114 and 143–63.

Argues that we can only understand the social policy issues confronting the Third World by understanding the nature of under-development. Chapters on health, social services and social planning are thus preceded by an analysis of the causes and consequences of underdevelopment.

3

The myth of mental illness?

INTRODUCTION

This chapter, like Chapter 2, is concerned with explanations. This time, however, the focus is on mental illness.

As with physical illness, the rates of mental illness change over time. Hysteria, for example, was a peculiarly Victorian disorder; today, depression is the mental condition that General Practitioners most frequently diagnose and treat. Rates of mental illness vary within societies as well. Hysteria was almost exclusively an affliction of white, middle- and upper-class women, aged between 15 and 40. Depression is also a predominantly female experience. One in ten men, but one in five women, are likely to be prescribed psychotropic drugs (drugs which affect the mind) in the course of a year and there are more than twice as many women as men admitted to Britain's mental hospitals suffering from depressive illnesses. Social class and social role again appear to play their part in depression, although the patterns are different to those associated with hysteria. It is working-class mothers who are most vulnerable to depression. Proportionally more working-class mothers are found to have symptoms of depression than middle-class mothers and working-class women without young children.

The distribution of mental illness follows the lines of colour as well as sex and class. West Indian men are more likely to be admitted to psychiatric hospital than white men, and black patients (Asian and West Indian) are more likely to be involuntary patients (Littlewood and Lipsedge, *Aliens and Alienists*, 1982, p. 65).

Confronted with such patterns, social scientists studying mental illness face the problem outlined in Chapter 2. In offering explanations of *individual* suffering, they have also to explain why *social* factors appear to be such powerful determinants of who suffers most.

As in the field of general welfare, explanations take two basic forms. First, there are those who argue that mental illness is a sign of individual weakness, stemming from a disorder in the body or the home life of the sufferer. Secondly, there are theories which see mental illness as created through the wider society, a product of the way in which material resources and professional services are distributed among the population. Conditions at work and in the home, patterns of treatment by doctors and social workers, these are seen as the causal factors in shaping an individual's experience of mental illness.

The two perspectives again are identified as victim-blaming and system-blaming explanations.

VICTIM-BLAMING THEORIES OF MENTAL ILLNESS

Victim-blaming theories tend to view mental illness as a disorder with identifiable causes which operate across a range of cultures. These causes are seen to lie in, or close to, the individual, in genetic endowment and brain chemistry, early childhood experiences and family relationships.

Such explanations of mental illness date back to the beginning of psychiatry. In fact, they are seen to be at the heart of the profession, providing the basis on which psychiatrists claim to know how to diagnose and treat the mentally ill. For an explanation of madness as an *individual* problem is essential if the kind of individual remedies available through psychiatry – drug treatment, ECT, psychotherapy and psychosurgery – are to be accepted and respected by society.

Psychiatry owes its victim-blaming perspective to medicine rather than the social sciences. While the study of suffering and unhappiness may seem to ally psychiatry closely to sociology, the discipline developed as a branch of medicine, dealing with 'diseases of the mind' while general medicine dealt with diseases of the body. In the nineteenth century, the brain was seen as the organ of the mind; for many, mental illnesses were cerebral illnesses. The theory that mental illnesses reflected physical disturbances in the brain – a lesion, perhaps, or a disease of the nervous system – dominated psychiatry for more than a century.

Today, still, there is a major concern with the classification of the symptoms and course of illness, and the hope that such classifications will reveal clear causes with measurable effects. The passage below is taken from a psychiatric textbook on neurosis which is considered to be the less serious type of psychiatric disorder and the one in which social factors may play the largest part. (In the passage, 'etiology' refers to the cause and 'diagnosis' to the definition and description of the disorder. 'Physiology' is the study of how the body functions, 'neurology' is the study of the nervous system, 'pharmacology' is the branch of medicine concerned with the preparation and effects of drugs and 'endocrinology' is concerned with the ductless glands which release hormones into the blood stream.)

Reading 1

The psychiatrist's methods and goals are similar to those of any other physician. He makes a diagnosis and treats, strives to reduce pain, lower discomfort and improve function. Basically, he deals with individuals: patients in treatment . . . Insight into the etiology of abnormal psychic states requires knowledge of the physiology of the nervous system, genetics, neurology, pharmacology, endocrinology and internal medicine. Thus, medical training is indispensable for the proper diagnosis and treatment of the mentally ill and psychiatric training is indispensable for proper diagnosis and treatment of the physically ill. Mind and body are inseparable . . .

Through the first quarter of the twentieth century the problems of classification, diagnosis, etiology and treatment of mental illness were far from settled. Yet, if psychiatry is ever to become a science, classification and diagnosis are essential . . . once etiology, diagnosis and classification are known, treatment becomes more rational. For example, paresis [partial paralysis] and pellagra [a vitamin deficiency disease] were two diseases whose diagnosis baffled physicians. Until bacteriologists identified *Treponema pallidum* – the organism responsible for paresis – and biochemists identified the deficiency in the vitamin niacin that caused pellagra, there was no satisfactory treatment for either disease. When etiology and diagnosis are specifically connected, the same situation could exist regarding other diseases that are now called mental. As long as diagnosis is in doubt, course and treatment are guesswork . . .

In comparison with the principles on which past classifications are based, modern day psychiatrists classify according to organic brain disease (organic brain syndrome), bodily disfunctions (psychophysical disorders), symptom etiology (neurosis and psychosis), intelligence (mental retardation) and deviant personality types . . .

M. Gray, *Neurosis: A Comprehensive Critical View*, 1978, pp. X, 31 and 44.

Questions

1. *What kind of knowledge does Gray suggest psychiatrists need to gain insight into the causes of mental illness? Would a sociologist add anything to this list?*

2. *From Gray's account, in what ways could psychiatry be described as 'victim-blaming'?*

3. *Gray suggests that, like physicians, psychiatrists deal with individuals.*
   Examine how this orientation might be reflected in the day-to-day work
   of a psychiatrist.

Within sociology, this model is rarely invoked to explain mental
illness. However, it is used to explain how psychiatrists see
mental illness. In other words, the victim-blaming model is used
by sociologists to illuminate the practice of psychiatry rather than
to identify the causes of mental illness. It is psychiatry, not
sociology, which is seen to believe in victim-blaming theories.

SYSTEM-BLAMING THEORIES OF MENTAL ILLNESS

While victim-blaming theories have long had a central place
within psychiatry, they have not gone unchallenged. Over the last
twenty years, a number of influential critiques of madness and
medicine have been launched by social scientists. These are seen
to have shaken the theoretical foundations of psychiatry,
tarnishing its image as a caring profession.

Central to the social scientist's critique is a relative conception
of mental illness. Mental illness is seen as an experience shaped
by social conditions and social expectations. The most powerful
critics go further: mental illness is shaped by the expectations of
the medical profession and the conditions in which they care for
those diagnosed as mentally ill.

Much of the theoretical ammunition for this attack on medicine
comes from the so-called labelling school. Writers like Thomas
Szasz and Thomas Scheff argue that mental illness only exists as a
metaphor. 'Mental illness' is a way of talking about social
problems, while at the same time disguising them and scapegoating the individuals who live through them.

Reading 2

It seems to me that in our scientific theories of behaviour we have
failed to accept the simple fact that human relations are
inherently fraught with difficulties and to make them even
relatively harmonious requires much patience and hard work. I
submit that the idea of mental illness is now being put to work to
obscure certain difficulties that at present may be inherent . . . in
the social intercourse of persons. If this is true, the concept
functions as a disguise: instead of calling attention to human
needs, aspirations and values, the concept of mental illness
provides an amoral and impersonal 'thing' – an 'illness' – as an

explanation for problems in living . . .

While I maintain that mental illnesses do not exist, I obviously do not imply or mean that the social and psychological occurrences to which the label is attached do not exist . . .

The expression 'mental illness' is a metaphor that we have come to mistake for a fact. We call people physically ill when their body-functioning violates certain anatomical and physiological norms; similarly, we call people mentally ill when their personal conduct violates certain ethical, political and social norms. This explains why many historical figures, from Jesus to Castro, and from Job to Hitler, have been diagnosed as suffering from this or that psychiatric malady.

Finally, the myth of mental illness encourages us to believe in its logical corollary: that social intercourse would be harmonious, satisfying and the secure basis of a good life were it not for the disrupting influences of mental illness, or psychopathology.

T. Szasz, 'The myth of mental illness', *American Psychologist*, 1960, pp. 113–18.

Questions
1. *How does Szasz see mental illness?*
2. *In what ways does his model differ from Gray's, described in Reading 1?*
3. *What does the author mean by 'the social and psychological occurrences' which the label of mental illness is used to describe?*

A major focus for labelling theorists has been the power of the medical profession. While arguing that mental illness is simply 'a form of words', once the process of labelling has been activated, it is seen to have real and long-lasting effects on its victims. It is these effects that Erving Goffman seeks to describe in *Asylums*, a participant-observation study of an American mental hospital. 'Degradation rituals' on admittance are designed to convince the patient that the psychiatrist's definition are the correct ones. The new in-patient is 'clearly stripped of many of his accustomed affirmations, satisfactions and defences, and is subjected to a rather full set of mortifying experiences . . . here one begins to learn about the limited extent to which a conception of oneself can be sustained when the usual setting of supports are suddenly removed' (*Asylums*, 1970, p. 137). Slowly, the patient is socialised into the world of madness. The staff know everything and can do anything, and in response the patient abandons any ideas of 'self' as something viable and defendable as a private space. Paradoxically, it is this 'mortification of self' which enables patients to survive, opening up the possibility of creating an 'underlife' invisible to, and yet within sight of, the hospital staff.

The passage below describes this underlife, as experienced by one patient, Connie, through her encounters with two fellow patients, Mrs Martinez and Sybil. The passage is taken from a novel.

Reading 3

On that Wednesday Connie was sitting . . . on her lap was spread yesterday's paper, a present from Fargo (the nurse) for cleaning up vomit, but she had read it through, including births and deaths and legal notices . . .

Mrs Martinez stood almost in front of her but a little to one side and fixed her eyes longingly on the newspaper, met her gaze questioningly, then glanced away. For months Mrs Martinez had not spoken. The attendants treated her as a piece of furniture. Many of the withdrawn had their own ways of speaking without words to anyone who was open, and Connie never had much trouble figuring out what Mrs Martinez wanted. She handed over the paper. 'Sure, I'm done reading it. But give it back, okay? For me to sit on.' A paper like that made a good pillow and she had no intention of abandoning it.

Connie was watching Martinez turn the pages slowly, when two orderlies brought in a woman handcuffed to a stretcher, trundling her past roaring muffled protest. A sheet was tied over her and only her hair was visible, long auburn hair clotted now with fresh blood. Her voice rose out of the sheet, her voice soared like a furious eagle flapping auburn wings.

'Sybil!' Connie cried out and half rose. Then she shut up. Giving nothing away. She watched them wrestle Sybil into seclusion . . .

Sitting quietly, Connie clasped her hands in her lap. Sybil was here. A slow warmth trickled through her. She had been lonely here, for few of the women on [ward] L–6 had energy left to relate, in their anguish of dealing with mommy, daddy, death, and the raw stuff of fear. She hoped the orderlies had not beaten her friend badly and that Sybil would simmer down and get out of seclusion soon. She had to try to get a message to Sybil through the locked door. Patients were not allowed to communicate with those in the isolation cells.

Her last time here they had met, and in the strange twilit

childhood of the asylum with its advancements and demotions, its privileges and punishments, its dreary air of grade school, they had twice been confined in the same ward long enough to become friends. Each patient rose and dropped through the dim rings of hell gaining and losing privileges, sent down to the violent wards, ordered to electroshock, filed away among the living cancers of the chronic wards, rewarded by convalescent status, allowed to do unpaid housework and go to dance therapy; but twice they had come to rest on the same step and they had talked and talked and talked their hearts to each other . . .

That morning she sat away from the station for privacy. When Sybil entered, looking tall and drawn, Connie did not greet her except with her eyes. It did not do to presume too much or to impose. Sometimes the mad behaved towards each other with delicate courtesy. She did not want to intrude on a desperate inner battle or mind loop. Sybil met her gaze, strolled the length of the ward in wary reconnaissance, then let her long body down beside her.

M. Piercy, *Women on the Edge of Time*, 1976, pp. 81–3.

Questions
1. *Describe the underlife in which Connie lives and communicates with her fellow inmates.*
2. *What do you think the author means by 'the strange twilit childhood of the asylum'?*

In *Asylums*, Goffman is concerned with the process of 'institutionalisation' and the ways in which people negotiate new 'mad' identities in situations of powerlessness. More recent writings on mental illness have moved away from the concern of labelling theorists with the practice of psychiatry. They reject the implication that mental illness is manufactured in mental hospitals, seeing it as a denial of suffering. They fear, too, that a sociology which says that mental illness is not real provides administrators with a rationale for doing little to improve the care of mental patients, either in hospital or in the community. The 'anti-psychiatry' movement is accused of turning its back on the needs of patients and their families, and joining with 'those who want to close down intensive psychiatric units and throw the victims on to the streets, with the occasional shot of tranquiliser injected in them to assure the public that something medical is still happening' (P. Sedgwick, *Psycho Politics*, 1982, p. 41).

In shifting their focus away from psychiatry, sociologists have begun to explore the social processes operating outside medicine which can create the feelings of worthlessness and hopelessness that we identify as depression. Their research suggests the way in which a lack of material resources (poverty, poor housing) and a lack of meaningful relationships (unemployment, isolation) are intimately related to a person's state of mind.

The most systematic attempt to uncover the links between social structure and self-esteem has been the study of *The Social Origins of Depression* by George Brown and Tirril Harris, based on nearly 600 women living in Camberwell, Greater London. Their research uncovered the marked class differences in the incidence of depression described at the beginning of the chapter. In explaining the class differences, they highlight two sets of factors. First, there is the experience of major life-events and difficulties, either of a long-term kind (like overcrowding, poverty and chronic ill-health) or of a more sudden nature (death, marriage breakdown). Secondly, there is the absence of factors which can help protect women faced with these problems; a confiding relationship with her husband, for example. The first group of factors Brown and Harris call 'provoking agents'; the second, they call 'protective factors' (if present) or 'vulnerability factors' (if absent).

In the reading below, George Brown outlines how these provoking agents and vulnerability factors combine to cause depression.

Reading 4

I believe that depression is essentially a social phenomenon . . . I would not make the same claim for schizophrenia, though its onset and course are also greatly influenced by social factors. Society and depression are more fundamentally linked. I can envisage societies where depression is absent and others where the majority suffer from depression . . .

Certain kinds of severe life-events and difficulties do appear to bring about the majority of depressive disorders – both among women treated by psychiatrists and among women found to be depressed after being selected at random from the general population. The kind of depression does not matter: these *provoking agents* are as strongly associated with the onset of psychotic as neurotic depressive conditions. Perhaps the most challenging claim of the model is that provoking agents (i.e. life-events and difficulties) are rarely sufficient to bring about depression – although they do determine *when* the disorders occur . . .

There is in fact a second set of factors. If a woman does not have an intimate relationship with a husband or boyfriend – one in which she feels she can confide and trust – she is much more likely to break down in the presence of a major life-event or difficulty. Similarly she is also at greater risk if she has three or more children under fifteen at home, if she is unemployed, and if she has lost her mother (but not her father) before the age of eleven. We call these *vulnerability factors* – although more optimistically they can be seen in a reverse way and called protective factors. None are capable of producing depression on their own, but they greatly increase chances of breakdown in the presence of a provoking agent. Some of the social class difference is explained by the fact that working-class women in London experience more untoward life-events and difficulties – in this sense their lives are much tougher. But most of the class difference is due to their excess of vulnerability factors which put working-class women at risk for depression at the time of a major life-event or difficulty.

> G. Brown, 'Depression: a sociological view' in D. Tuckett and J. Kaufert (eds), *Basic Readings in Medical Sociology*, 1978, pp. 225–30.

Questions

1. *Describe, in your own words or in a diagram, Brown and Harris's model of depression.*
2. *Which set of factors do the authors identify as the more important in causing depression: provoking agents or vulnerability factors?*
3. *What are the implications of Brown and Harris's theory for the prevention and treatment of depression?*
4. *What are its implications for the kind of psychiatry described in Reading 1?*

Brown and Harris demonstrate that 'there *is* a link between clinical depression and a woman's daily experience' (*The Social Origins of Depression*, 1978, p. 4). But they do not examine how women's depression and women's daily lives may themselves be linked to women's position in society. This deeper analysis of social structure has not been neglected, however.

Since the early 1970s, the issue of women and madness has been widely explored by such writers as Susan Lipshitz (Reading 5) and Phyllis Chesler (*Women and Madness*). The greater vulnerability of women to mental illness has led them to enquire whether the traditional roles allocated to women create particular 'problems of living' which are more readily identified as symptoms of madness than the problems experienced by men.

This hypothesis has been explored in many ways. For example, it is argued that psychiatry operates with not one but two concepts of mental health. Mental health for men means adjustment to masculinity, to independence and to coping in a competitive and aggressive world. Such tendencies in women, however, are seen as symptoms of mental illness, signalling a failure to accept their feminine role. Healthy women are expected to be dependent and emotional, and excitable in a crisis. Yet, at the same time, these characteristics are also the ones ascribed to the mentally ill. Our definitions of femininity and madness, it seems, are inextricably linked. For women, therefore, neither 'feminine' nor 'masculine' traits serve to safeguard their sanity.

Reading 5

Just how different is the diagnosed 'mental health' of men and women? We get some indication of the official situation from figures of diagnoses at hospital admission in Britain . . .

The figures indicate that women are categorised more often than men as depressed, psychoneurotic, psychotic, or as suffering from non-specific disorders. That is to say they turn feelings in on themselves rather than expressing them openly, and are characterised by states of retreat like the psychoses. These statistics are not surprising if we think of the image of women in our society. For stereotypic femininity describes women as more passive, weak, expressive of emotion, dependent, illogical and living in a world of feelings and far more concerned with their own appearance than are men. The male stereotype emphasises competence, activity, analytic ability and independence – all characteristics that are considered to be both socially desirable and adult.

Broverman et al[1] investigated American clinicians' perceptions of healthy functioning and its relationship to the patient's sex, using a questionnaire that listed stereotypic characteristics of both sexes. They were able to show that male and female clinicians shared an implicit model of the female. There was a contradiction between the demands of femininity and the demands of adult health. A 'healthy woman' was implicitly expected to be a non-coping childish being in need of protection, emotionally volatile and thus not an independent adult. Female patients suffering partly from the restrictive definition of the feminine stereotype are confronted with treatment which may not only reinforce these restrictions but presents them as *ideals*.

In the light of this, the hospital admission figures . . . can be explained by the different standards for male and female health and by the different opportunities offered by the stereotypes for the expression and display of particular symptoms and illness. Women's illnesses conform to the stereotyped ways in which women are expected to handle anger and frustration, and women coming into hospital unable to cope are diagnosed in accordance with what would be expected in terms of the stereotype . . . The comparable stereotypic 'deviance' for men seems to be their criminal behaviour; from the age of fourteen onwards more males commit criminal offences. However, it would be over-simplifying the issue of illness or criminality to argue that a similar dynamic can be said to underlie both.

1. I. Broverman, D. Broverman, F. Clarkson, P. Rosenkrantz and S. Vogel, 'Sex Role Stereotypes and Clinical Judgements of Mental Health', *Journal of Consulting and Clinical Psychology*, 1970, 34, pp. 1–7.

   S. Lipshitz, 'Women and psychiatry' in J. Chetwynd and O. Hartnett, *The Sex Role System*, 1978, pp. 95–7.

Questions

1. *According to Reading 5, what is the stereotype of masculinity and femininity in society?*
2. *In what ways is the stereotype of femininity found reflected in medicine and psychiatry?*
3. *What does Lipshitz mean by the statement 'there was a contradiction between the demands of femininity and the demands of adult health'?*
4. *What links does the author suggest between mental illness and crime?*

The question of women's particular relation to the welfare state is addressed again in Chapters 6 and 7. The next chapter, however, considers the position of both men and women who find themselves on the receiving end of Britain's health and welfare services.

ESSAY QUESTIONS

1. Read the following passage and answer the questions which follow.

   It is possible to raise the question, 'is there such a thing as mental illness?' and to argue that there is not. In maintaining that mental illness does not exist, one is not implying that the social or psychological occurrences to which this label is attached do not exist. Like the personal and social troubles that people had in the Middle Ages, contemporary human problems are real enough. It is the labels that we give them that are important and having labelled them, what we do about them. The demonological concept of problems in living gave rise to treatment along medical or psychotherapeutic lines. The expression 'mental illness' is a metaphor that we have come to mistake for a fact. We call people physically ill when their body-functioning violates anatomical and physiological norms; similarly we call people mentally ill when their personal conduct violates certain ethical, political and social norms – many historical figures have been diagnosed as suffering from this or that psychiatric malady.

The currently prevailing position according to which psychiatrists treat mental illness and disease is that the latter are just as 'real' and 'objective' as bodily diseases. This is a kind of psychiatric propaganda: their aim is to create, in the popular mind, a confident belief that mental illness is some sort of disease entity like an infection or a malignancy. If this were true, one could catch or get a mental illness, and one could finally get rid of it.

(a) Explain what is meant by the statement, 'the expression "mental illness" is a metaphor that we can come to mistake for a fact.' (lines 11–12)

(b) Give two examples of the way in which people are labelled 'mentally ill' when their personal conduct violates certain ethical or political or social norms. (lines 14–16)

(c) Briefly outline the basic assumptions underlying the view of mental illness outlined in the passage. (JMB, 1981)

2. Outline and evaluate any *one* sociological contribution to the study of mental illness. (AEB, 1982).

3. 'We must see the mental hospital as one among a network of institutions designed to provide residence to various categories of socially troublesome people' (I. Goffman, *Asylums*). Examine and evaluate the evidence for this statement.

4. Examine the relationship between mental illness and *either* social class *or* gender. How have sociologists explained the relationship?

FURTHER READING

1. G. Pearson, *The Deviant Imagination*, Macmillan, 1975, pp. 15–17 and 25–31.

Discusses the power of psychiatry and medicine in the treatment of deviance and the assault made by anti-psychiatry on it, looking in particular at Thomas Szasz's claim that mental illness is a myth.

2. A. Oakley, *Subject Woman*, Fontana, 1982, pp. 75–81.

Describes the way in which women's mental instability has been represented in history, the current rates of mental illness among women and men, and how these sex differences can be explained.

3. R. Littlewood and M. Lipsedge, *Aliens and Alienists: Ethnic Minorities and Psychiatry*, Penguin, 1982, pp. 37–67.

Examines the evidence for arguing that Western medicine is built on a structure of beliefs which make it predisposed to define black people as mentally ill.

4. E. Freidson, 'The institutional organisation of being ill' in P. Worsley (ed), *Problems of Modern Society*, Penguin, 1978, pp. 601–6.

Describes how illness is defined and controlled in medical institutions.

5. J. King and G. Brown, 'Institutionalism and schizophrenia: summary, discussion and conclusions' in D. Tuckett and J. Kaufert (eds), *Basic Readings in Medical Sociology*, Tavistock, 1978.

Tests out the idea that the symptoms exhibited by schizophrenic patients in mental hospitals are a product of their environment. The authors conclude there is considerable evidence to support this view.

4

Poor clients and sick patients: the experience of welfare

INTRODUCTION: DEPENDENCY AND STIGMA

The first three chapters have been principally concerned with poverty and ill-health and not with the poor and the ill. This chapter examines the ways in which their lives are represented within sociology.

Sociologists have generally had more to say about the roles occupied by the poor and the sick than about the experience of suffering itself. Moreover, it is not the poor role and the sick role that has interested sociologists so much as the narrower and more specific roles the poor and sick occupy in their dealings with professionals. The poor thus tend to figure as claimants and clients and the sick as patients. This focus reflects sociology's concern with social order and its view that the poor and sick, living outside the mainstream culture geared to able-bodied wage-earning families, are deviants. Sociologists are interested therefore in the way in which the roles of the poor and the sick are shaped to ensure that any challenges to society are successfully contained. It is the welfare services (social security, social work and medicine) which are seen to play a major part in this shaping process. Specifically, these services are seen as crucially linked to the stigma and the dependency associated with sickness and poverty.

The word 'stigma' originally referred to the mark physically branded onto slaves and criminals. Today, it is seen as a symbolic mark of discredit ascribed to individuals who possess 'an undesired differentness' which makes others believe they are 'not quite human' (Goffman, *Stigma*, 1968, p. 15). Sociologists in the interactionist tradition have studied the psychological effects that stigma can have on identity and have noted how individuals seek to control the negative images that others have of them through a process of 'impression management'. More recently, sociologists have used the concept of stigma to understand the structural position of the poor and the ill. They link stigma to dependency. It is those groups who are dependent on others for their survival

who are seen as particularly vulnerable to stigma. Thus, financial
dependency is a powerful factor in stigma. Being jobless and
'living off the state' is common to many stigmatised groups;
unemployed school-leavers, single mothers with young children
and the elderly all experience this kind of economic dependency.
Physical dependency is also associated with stigma. Physically
and mentally handicapped people who are dependent on the care
of others often feel themselves to be treated as 'not quite
human'. This explains one reason why those unable to live
independently are often reluctant to go into old people's homes
and mental hospitals, institutions which seem to symbolise their
inferior status.

In looking at economic and physical dependency, sociologists
have begun to question how much dependency (and the stigma
attached to it) is inherent in the condition itself. Prompted by the
self-help organisations of the old and disabled, they have begun
to enquire whether, instead, dependency is created through our
treatment of those who are deemed to have 'an undesired
differentness'. It is this complex question of the nature of
dependency that is raised in the passage below. Old age is a
condition associated in the public mind with physical and
economic dependency, with needing to be 'looked after'. Yet the
author argues that dependency is not so much the result of
physical deterioration as of enforced retirement. In so doing, the
author challenges the usefulness of such labels as 'old age', seeing
it instead as part of the process which singles out some people as
'not quite human'.

Reading 1

In this paper I wish to put forward the thesis that the dependency
of the elderly in the twentieth century is being manufactured
socially . . . Certain major influences are steadily deepening or
widening that dependency. There is the imposition and acceptance of earlier retirement; the legitimation of low income; the
denial of rights to self-determination in institutions; and the
construction of community services for recipients assumed to be
predominantly passive . . .

Retirement has become a social phenomenon of vast importance in the short span of the last fifty years . . . Between 40 per
cent and 70 per cent of men aged 65 and over in all industrial
countries were still economically active in the 1930s. But by the
mid-1960s, with the exception of Japan, the proportion had
shrunk dramatically to between 10 per cent and 40 per
cent . . . This change cannot be attributed to changes in the risk
of ill-health or disability, or the masking of disability in periods
before pensions were available. It is attributable to changes in the

organisation of work and in the kinds of people wanted for work . . . Problems have arisen for companies and unions which can only be resolved by a kind of mass redundancy, which retirement has become. Retirement is in a real sense a euphemism for unemployment . . . The institutionalisation of pensions and services has also paid a major part . . . State pensions and other cash benefits comprise the most important source of income for the elderly in most advanced industrial societies and [these] . . . tend to be low relative to the earnings of younger adults. In Britain, various studies put the net incomes of [retired] married couples at less than half of younger non-retired people . . . Pension levels are defined in relation to subsistence needs, and are usually pitched considerably below earnings . . . [This explains why] so many people descend into poverty or near poverty after retirement.* . . .

The engineering of retirement and mass poverty among the elderly in the twentieth century are, of course, linked, and they have been pre-eminent in creating the social dependency of the elderly. But their connection with the development of residential and community care is too frequently overlooked. The assumptions of all the participants [in residential and community care] are greatly affected by the facts of retirement and poverty. They govern the attitudes and the actions of the professional staff on the one hand and elderly clients or residents on the other . . .

The majority of residents in homes are placed in a category of enforced dependence. The routine of residential homes, made necessary by small staffs and economical administration, and committed to an ideology of care and attention rather than the encouragement of self-help and self-management seems to deprive many residents of the opportunity to occupy themselves and even of the means of communication . . .

[Within the community care services] day centres are sometimes organised on the same lines as residential homes, but without residence at night . . . The duties of home helps and community nurses are also heavily circumscribed. The elderly are usually viewed as the grateful and passive recipients of services administered by an enlightened public authority. This can but reinforce their dependency both in their own eyes and that of the public.

* nearly two-thirds of the elderly (about 5 million people) live in or on the margins of poverty.

P. Townsend, 'The structured dependency of the elderly', *Ageing and Society*, 1981, pp. 5, 10, 12, 20 and 22.

Questions

1. *What evidence does Townsend put forward to support his argument that the dependency of the elderly is socially created?*
2. *What other factors could explain the dependency of the elderly?*
3. *In what ways does Townsend find the economic dependency of the elderly (their poverty and their status as retired workers) reflected in residential and community care?*
4. *What sorts of social policies would be needed to reverse the socially-created dependency of the elderly?*

Reading 1 points to the way in which the organisation of the labour market can force people into dependent and stigmatising positions. More important for our discussion here, however, is Peter Townsend's argument that the provision of welfare (pensions, residential care, community care) can have the same effect. This leaves claimants, clients and patients in a 'Catch-22' situation. On the one hand, the welfare professions provide life-sustaining services: money, housing, health care. On the other, however, they do so by involving their clients in relationships which can further undermine their social status and their self-esteem.

This crucial issue, of the roles created for the needy within the welfare state, is examined in the two sections below. The first looks at management of the poor within the welfare state, where the majority of those in long-term poverty rely on selective benefits provided to those who can demonstrate a need. The second section looks at the management of the sick in the National Health Service, a service provided on a universal basis to all, regardless of income.

CLAIMANTS AND CLIENTS IN THE WELFARE STATE

In seeking to understand the experiences of the poor, the major writers have adopted a strongly historical perspective on the welfare state. An appreciation of provision in the past is seen as essential for an appreciation of the social security system in the present. For some writers, our present system is the legacy of an administrative framework dating back to 1945 and the Beveridge plan for universal insurance 'to take the place of earnings when they are interrupted by unemployment, sickness or accident' (*Report on Social Insurance and Allied Services*, p. 120). For others, the social security system is seen to reflect an older apparatus of relief for the poor, the Poor Law.

In eighteenth- and nineteenth-century England, state provision for the poor was of the most basic and limited kind (Chapter 2, pp. 26–8 describes the kind of theories which legitimated this level of provision). The underlying approach to poverty was enshrined

in the Poor Law Act of 1834, seen by most social scientists as a
landmark in the development of the welfare state.

Despite its name, the Poor Law Act was not designed to
eliminate poverty; its aim was not to provide services, in cash or
kind, to bring the living standards of the poor up to an acceptable
minimum (as the social security system aims to do today). Its
primary concern was not with poverty, but with pauperism. It
aimed to deter poor families from giving up the struggle to
survive on their own and turning to the state for support.

The distinction between the poor (who were poor but
independent) and the paupers (who had no means of livelihood)
was fundamental to state provision after 1834. The pre-1834
system of allowances for the needy was seen to have blurred this
central distinction, by being set at such a high level that they
encouraged workers 'to quit the less eligible [i.e. desirable] class
of labourers and enter the more eligible class of paupers' (*Report
of the 1834 Poor Law Commissioners*, 1834, p. 228).

To remedy this situation, the 1834 Act abolished the allowance
system, leaving only the workhouse for the destitute. Conditions
in the workhouse were determined by the principle of 'less
eligibility'. Paupers, in failing to provide for themselves and their
dependants, had proved themselves unworthy of the full rights of
British citizenship. The state denied them the vote and ensured
that the support it provided was less attractive than that secured
through the low and intermittent wages on which large sections of
the population lived. According to one Poor Law commissioner,
workhouses aimed to establish 'a discipline so severe and
repulsive as to make them a terror to the poor and prevent them
from entering'. Through the workhouse, the 1834 Act thus
institutionalised a division within the working class between the
undeserving paupers and the working poor. State help for
paupers was provided only if they submitted themselves to the
indignity and 'repulsive discipline' of the workhouse.

Reading 2

Until the last quarter of the nineteenth century provision for the
poor in Great Britain was founded on the poor law of 1834
supplemented by individual philanthropy. To the well-to-do 'the
poor' were a race apart, inevitable but unpleasant like sin or
death, to be tolerated and pitied, or to be despised if they fell
into the hideous category of 'paupers'. Pauperism meant more
than misfortune, it implied a moral failing. Those who accepted
parochial aid were legally assumed to be guilty of sin, of laziness
and improvidence. They were less eligible for the privileges of
citizenship than their fellows and as such were deprived of the
franchise or, in fact, of their personal freedom by being required

to accept parish aid under semi-penal conditions in the poor house.

The 'respectable' working class shared the view of the well-to-do about pauperism, if not about the poor. But if the prosperous despised the individuals, the worker feared the condition. The bricklayer, the miner, the mechanic, the carpenter, knew that old age, or accident to himself, a technological improvement, the failure of his provident society or trade union, or the malfeasance of its treasurer, might throw him and his family onto the poor law. Economic security was a condition he and his fellows would never know, but he despised paupers no less than the wealthy on this account. Victorian England succeeded so well in making the term 'the poor law' a phrase of abuse that social reformers of the twentieth century were unable to cleanse these words of their disparaging connotations. As a result, when the welfare state began to grow, practically all the vast nineteenth-century apparatus of parochial relief had to be abandoned lest it taint the new reform measures.

B. Gilbert, *The Evolution of National Insurance in Great Britain*, 1973, pp. 21–2.

Questions

1. *How were the poor and paupers viewed in mid-nineteenth-century Britain?*
2. *Why did the 'respectable' working class both fear and despise paupers?*
3. *To what extent does Gilbert's account of the images of wealth and poverty prevalent in Victorian England lend support to Holman's view that the existence of poverty helps maintain the social order? (See Reading 5, Chapter 2.)*

While Gilbert suggests that the apparatus of the nineteenth-century Poor Law was demolished by the twentieth-century reforms, other writers argue that its basic principles were unchanged.

Beveridge planned to provide the population with protection from the risk of poverty and want 'from the cradle to the grave' through a new social insurance system. In return for one weekly payment, an employed man was eligible to benefit during old age, sickness and unemployment. Beveridge envisaged that the insurance system would become universal, but in the short term it needed the support of a system of selective means-tested allowances. This was called National Assistance, today's Supplementary Benefit. Means-tested benefits were required to bring insurance payments up to subsistence level and to cater for those like the long-term unemployed, the old and women without a male breadwinner who had paid insufficient insurance premiums to be eligible for benefit. While Beveridge saw the survival of the means test as temporary, the number of means-tested benefits has increased not diminished. So, too, has the number of people dependent upon them. In 1948, less than one million people were claiming National Assistance; thirty-three years later, the Supplementary Benefit system had three million clients (when their dependants are included, the number of people living on supplementary benefit was five million). Further, this figure excludes the large numbers of people who do not claim the benefits to which they are entitled. It is estimated that Supplementary Benefit, for example, is claimed by only 70 per cent of those eligible for it (Deacon and Bradshaw, *Reserved for the Poor*, 1983, p. 124). While the reasons for non-take-up are complex, one important factor identified is stigma. Selectivism, and the stigma of pauperism, have been perpetuated within a system designed to be universal in its coverage and non-stigmatising in its effects. As one claimant put it in a study by John Mayer and Noel Timms (*The Client Speaks*, 1970, p. 102), quoted in more detail later in the chapter:

> It's very degrading getting help. You feel that everyone is against you and won't talk to you, because you're nothing. I would be standing and having a chat with friends and as they walked away, I would say to myself, well, you're down and everyone is against you. Afterwards, of course, you realize that they know nothing about your affairs, but at the time you feel very low. It's a terrible feeling.

The distinction between the 'deserving' and 'undeserving' poor has been detected not only in the operation of the social security system, but in the personal social services. Social work, for example, is seen primarily as a service for 'problem families' within the working class who are unable to support themselves or care adequately for their families. Clients, like claimants, thus find themselves isolated from their non-client neighbours who maintain their respectability by surviving independently of the state. The passage below identifies some of the factors that contribute to the isolation and stigma experienced by those on the receiving end of professional help. 'Intra-class' means within the class; 'inter-class' means between the social classes.

Reading 3

The physical and moral distance which so often separates clients from non-clients within the same community and which can lead to intra-class tension arises from a complex of interacting issues. Some of these are all too obvious, such as the policies pursued by some local housing authorities in isolating 'problem families' in physically distinct hard-to-let ghetto housing. Then there are the wider problems of surviving poverty. For many clients the struggle to survive is time-consuming and exhausting, instanced by endless hours of bargain-hunting, managing with few or no domestic appliances, coping with inadequate methods for heating rooms and water, plus all the other struggles over clothing, housing, washing and food. For many of the dependent poor their diets deteriorate to such an extent that their health declines and lethargy and depression result. Factors such as these greatly inhibit clients' possibilities for social interaction and their involvement in local tenant and community groups, and for many the sheer lack of cash closes off other points of contact such as the local pub, cafe or club. High transport costs have also heightened this isolation through reducing the mobility of those on low incomes or dependent on state benefits.

These are a few of the factors which can help to an understanding of the isolation of many clients. The apparent individualism of many clients and their subsequent distancing from their neighbours and local communities is therefore not so much a symptom of their 'inadequate' personality but rather the consequences of survival in a largely hostile and uncaring society . . .

For those neighbours who have been inconvenienced by living next door to a family whose house is deteriorating, whose children are noisy until the early hours of the morning, and so on and so forth, the sight of seeing a social worker visiting can be a cause of outrage. This outrage can be compounded if they see the social worker delivering 'goodies' (e.g. furniture) of one sort or another or arranging special programmes and treats for the youngsters, as their own material circumstances may be little better than that of the neighbours who receive such help. Their survival independent of the help of state agencies may be, and often is, very difficult and hard. Yet there is no public acknowledgement of their 'citizenly' virtues and sacrifice. It could seem to them that there is much to be gained from being a nuisance, deviant or a problem for the state. Instead of having to struggle and scrimp for furniture and clothing, instead of living in dread of the next fuel or rates bill, instead of having to think of how to give the children a holiday or occupy them in the evening, it may be better to give up and call in the social services.

C. Jones, *State Social Work and the Working Class*, 1983, pp. 57 and 53.

Questions
1. *How does Jones explain the isolation of clients?*
2. *In what ways does his explanation lend support to a materialist or structuralist explanation of poverty (outlined in Chapter 2)?*
3. *How does Jones explain the hostility that can exist between clients and non-clients in working-class communities? Do you think the same processes would be at work in middle-class communities?*

Relationships, not only within the community, but with the personal social services, can reinforce the sense of isolation and stigma. As one observer notes of the client, 'having once embarked on a career as a social work client, she is in constant jeopardy as a mother, for her every action is being observed and judged, not only (as in social security) for its deservingness, but also for its parental quality' (Jordan, *Poor Parents*, 1974, p. 132). Like social security officers, social workers are in a position both to provide help and to pass judgements. While professional help can directly improve the quality of a client's life, the way in which it is provided can, at the same time, further undermine her self-confidence and self-respect. The effect of these conflicting pressures on claimants, both to accept and to resist help from social services, is reflected in the patterns of interaction recorded beween professionals and their clients. Those consigned to powerless positions seek to exert control through the subtle process of 'impression management'.

Reading 4
These clients tended to believe that their (social) workers would be contemptuous of their financial dependency or, worse yet, look upon them as cadgers. Given these perceptions, we would suppose that they did their best to become 'de-classified' – to become viewed as 'different', as persons who did not *really* belong in the client category. Any success they achieved – which essentially involved efforts to appear 'deserving' – would presumably help them to preserve their self-respect, to say nothing of yielding (or hopefully yielding) financial benefits . . .

This emphasis on 'impression management' is perhaps fairly general among clients in need of material help . . . Those in search of material assistance sought to ingratiate themselves with the worker. To some extent they did things they did not want to do in order to appear 'deserving'. Efforts of this type are apt to be successful. More significantly, they are apt to generate feelings of self-disgust, which in time become converted into anger and resentment towards those 'responsible' for their self-contempt. Thus, it seems perfectly understandable why Mrs Denton [one of the clients in the study], who felt she 'had lowered herself and still got nowhere', 'never said goodbye or thank you' to the worker.

> J. Mayer and N. Timms, *The Client Speaks: Working Class Impressions of Casework*, 1970, pp. 131–3.

Questions

1. *Why might the clients in the study wish to 'declassify' themselves?*
2. *What techniques did they employ in order to appear 'deserving'?*
3. *What affect do you think clients' attempts at impression management have on their social workers?*

Impression management is apparent, too, among clients seeking non-financial help. In the account below, the client and her husband, David, are seeking to adopt their second child. They have a new social worker, Miss R, who has had one interview with the client and her already-adopted child, Jane. They have just had a letter to say that their application for adoption, once approved by the Adoption Committee, must go before the Committee again.

> The letter came as a bombshell. As the Committee had already approved our application for a second child our interpretation was that Miss R, in one interview with Jane and me, must have decided that we were not suitable. I was so angry and so panic-stricken that I hardly knew what to do first . . . I felt very hostile towards Miss R but obviously this had to be concealed which went very much against the grain. David telephoned her and went to see her the same day. I begged him to try and be nice to her. We had far too much at stake to be able to afford the luxury of plain speaking – or so we thought at the time. For the first time in my life I really knew what it felt like to feel helpless in the hands of a social agency and be dependent on the goodwill and competence of a social worker in whom I had so little confidence (Timms, *The Receiving End*, 1973, p. 34).

In detailing the negative experiences of clients and claimants, sociologists are not simply concerned with exposing 'bad' social workers, they are concerned with a whole structure of relationships which surround those identified as having financial and social problems. Similarly, sociologists who have studied people's experiences of medical care are not primarily concerned with identifying nice (and nasty) doctors. They are seeking to understand the relation between the patient and his or her illness on the one hand, and, on the other, the formal and informal networks of support provided by the state and the community.

PATIENTS IN THE NATIONAL HEALTH SERVICE

Sociologists have identified a number of important differences in the position of patient and clients in the welfare state. First, while patients and clients may both have abandoned their normal wage-earning responsibilities, patients are rarely accused of 'sponging' and 'scrounging'. For patients, their illness and disability legitimates dependency. In Talcott Parsons's words, 'illness is predominantly a withdrawal into a dependent relationship, it is asking to be "taken care of ". It uses disability as the basis of legitimation of this claim' (*The Social System*, 1951, p. 285). Secondly, unlike the social services, the National Health Service is a universal service, financed through taxation and accessible to all. It is thus seen to avoid the losses of individual dignity associated with the selective systems of income maintenance and personal social services.

These two factors, the socially-accepted status of the patient and the non-discriminatory system of health care provision, suggest that the experience of being a patient will be a less demoralising and isolating experience than that of being a client.

Questions of stigma and social control, however, are still raised, particularly in patients' dealings with health professionals. Doctors, in the surgery and the hospital, have the knowledge and expertise that patients need; further, they decide whether and how their knowledge will be shared and their expertise applied. In seeking to understand how the roles of doctor and patient are sustained, often against the wishes of the participants, sociologists have pointed to the importance of the professional hierarchies in medicine and the physical layout of surgeries and hospitals which put patients, literally and symbolically, in their place.

Reading 5

Clients may be controlled by what may be termed the dramatic structuring of their encounters with professionals. This dramatic structuring is normally largely in the hands of the professional and is probably at its strongest in the hospital setting. For

example, the parent bringing a child to a combined clinic for
spina bifida, faces a variety of waits in crowded waiting rooms,
surrounded by a continual bustle of coming and going with
nurses, and others who are often less readily identifiable, passing
to and fro with notes, messages, trays, etc. When the mother
enters the consultation room she is faced by a white-coated
doctor often behind his desk, sometimes surrounded by some of
the esoteric symbols of his profession. He may well also have a
deferential bevy of medical students, an odd nurse and maybe a
visitor or two (at least she presumes that's who they are because
she is rarely introduced to them). They may well talk to each
other in an esoteric language during the consultation. In that
situation the consultant clearly controls the whole encounter.
Everyone waits on his questions, actions and movements.
Frequently he will ask questions of the mother with little
explanation of their relevance and will make little attempt to
explain what he makes of the answers. Taken *in toto* a very
powerful message of the importance, business and strange
expertise of the doctor are spelt out and the parent who feels
sufficiently at home, confident and significant to take an active
part in what is going on is probably the exception. It is no wonder
that many take little advantage of it even when asked if they have
any questions. Such structuring is probably equally powerful in
the supplementary benefits office and only a little less effective in
the GP's surgery, the employment exchange and the school. It is
certainly at its weakest when the social worker makes a home
visit because here the client is on his own territory and the
professional can call on few esoteric symbols of his status. About
all he can fall back on is a fully self-confident performance.
Precisely because such an encounter is routine for him but usually
not for the client, if he simply acts with authority he may well
take charge of the proceedings without necessarily intending it.

   T. Robinson, *In Worlds Apart: Professionals and their Clients in the
   Welfare State*, 1978, p. 39.

Questions
1. *In what ways is the patient controlled in medical consultations?*
2. *What effect is this process of social control likely to have on patients?*
3. *In what ways might patients attempt to resist?*

Empirical studies have described how this 'dramatic structuring' works in practice. The studies suggest, too, that those groups in the population who have the highest incidence of sickness suffer most from the structuring of the patient role. Working-class patients appear to be more effectively silenced than middle-class patients. Cartwright and O'Brien (*The Sociology of the National Health Service*, 1976, pp. 89 and 91) found that middle-class patients discussed more problems and spent longer talking to their doctors. Their doctors, who are themselves predominantly middle class, felt that middle-class patients were less likely to bring 'inappropriate' problems to them than working-class patients. The silencing of patients appears not only to operate along the lines of social class. Gender, too, has been identified as a factor which structures doctor–patient interaction. As noted in Chapter 3, definitions of mental health can be sex-specific, with the result that women can find themselves more at risk of being defined as mentally ill. Evidence suggests that a person's skin colour as well as their sex can influence the style and outcome of interaction. Black patients have been found to talk more and in more depth if their doctors share their ethnic background. Doctors, for their part, appear to perceive and respond to black patients differently, classifying them more often as mentally disturbed, for example (Littlewood and Lipsedge, *Aliens and Alienists*, 1982, p. 65).

While it is important to recognise the processes by which patients are controlled in their dealings with welfare professionals, it is equally important not to overlook the benefits provided by the National Health Service, and the welfare services more generally. Again, sociologists have turned to history to highlight the very real way in which the welfare state has helped those struggling to maintain the health of their families on a low income. For many working-class families, and for many women, the welfare state has provided resources which have improved their standard of living.

The reading below describes some results of a survey conducted in the 1930s, before the introduction of the National Health Service in Britain. The survey was based on 1250 working-class wives, and focuses on their housing, their housework, their diet and their health. The passage explores the reasons why mothers fail to take their health problems to their doctors.

Reading 6

The most important factor [why women do not seek medical advice when unwell] . . . is poverty, especially in those illnesses which the woman thinks she can fairly safely overlook, such as headaches, constipation, anaemia and bad teeth. Here is a typical example of this attitude, governed by lack of funds. A woman in Preston aged 30 has had three children, the eldest of whom died in infancy. Her husband is unemployed. She has 27/3d house-keeping money, and is in a very bad house, which has no sink. She suffers from constipation, headaches, faintness and 'low condition'. 'I go to bed early with the children and get up late to save coal and food.' She says, 'I went to see Clinic Doctor. She advised me to go to own Doctor and get a tonic, said I was undernourished and run down, owe Doctor 2 accounts so shall not go.' Another example comes from Mrs F. of Sheffield. She is 47 and has had seven children, of whom two have died. Her husband is a railway drayman. She gets £2 17. 0d. housekeeping (including £1 from one son of 23 who lives at home 'but eats a lot'). She has rheumatism, (since she had an operation for gall-stones two years ago), toothache, headache and back-ache. For none of these does she consult anyone. She owes her private doctor for the last five years' attendance, including the last confinement, £14, which she pays off in 1/- weekly instalments collected by a collector . . .

Rheumatism, gynaecological troubles and bad legs being much more crippling to work, show a larger percentage of advice sought and treatment taken. Gynaecological trouble has other features in respect of treatment. The woman probably does not recognise the symptoms herself. ('Backache since birth of baby'. 'Internal trouble through confinements', are frequent complaints for which no advice and treatment have been sought), and in the absence of a thorough post-natal examination, the trouble is not discovered till the birth of the next child, often not then if she has not been attended by a doctor. When it is discovered, much greater pressure is brought to bear on her by the doctor or nurse to have the matter attended to . . .

The comparative percentages for professional treatment in the seven specially analysed ailments are:-

Headaches	30% are professionally treated		
Constipation	36% "	"	"
Anaemia	38% "	"	"
Bad teeth	43% "	"	"
Rheumatism	56% "	"	"
Gynaecological trouble	59% "	"	"
Bad legs	60% "	"	"

The best of these figures shows a deplorably low percentage of treatment and it is not entirely explained by poverty, or a courageous neglect. There is also a good deal of prejudice and/or fear due to ignorance . . . A woman with fibroid on the uterus has been advised to have hysterectomy performed, but her husband is unwilling. She is 38 and has eight children already. A woman of 36 with ten children refuses to go to hospital for 'uterine trouble' . . . 'because of children'. The Health Visitor says she has argued with her after each confinement, but it is useless, 'I think it is prejudice' . . . Another with severe vaginal discharge, which has lasted some years, has had seven children. She says she 'would consult a Doctor for a definite illness, which would have to be paid for out of housekeeping money'. A woman from an outlying district of London writes:- 'I went after my operation, but they have no proper women's out-patient department and the man doctor used to come out to me in the waiting-room and asked me how I was feeling. I could not tell him why I had come to see him as I had two youths sitting beside me, so I said I was quite well and went away. I cannot go to the doctor who told me to go to the hospital; I only went to him first because I didn't know where else to go. He is a young bachelor and will not examine me unless I take someone with me and as I have no friends on the new estate this is too difficult; besides I can't talk to a young man about such intimate affairs. I think a woman must have a woman doctor for these things, and we would not have so much trouble if we did.' This is not prejudice, but a clear indication of where the medical service for women needs development.

M. Spring-Rice, *Working Class Wives: their Health and Conditions*, 1939, pp. 40–3.

Questions

1. *What kinds of ailments does the author identify among her respondents?*
2. *What factors deter them from seeking medical care?*
3. *What light does the survey shed on the process by which a person becomes a patient (see Chapter 1, Reading 3)? Does the evidence suggest that social networks and social roles are important in this process?*

In discussing the experiences of working-class women prior to the National Health Service, Margery Spring-Rice touches on a major issue of controversy within sociology and social policy. Controversy rages about whether the NHS, and the welfare state as a whole, has achieved its objectives. Has it achieved greater equality of access? Has it improved the national health? Is it more efficient than alternative systems for the distribution of medical care? These questions are the subject of Chapter 5.

ESSAY QUESTIONS

1. The following is an account of a series of interviews between a client and practitioners in the Family Welfare Association. How might a sociologist analyse the client–practitioner interaction described in the passage?

Mrs Wilson is twenty-three years old and the mother of two children. At the time of these interviews, her husband was in prison on a six-month sentence. She went to the Family Welfare Association because she was having difficulty 'making ends meet' and above all wanted help with a large electricity bill. In order to make sense of Mrs Wilson's reactions to treatment, one must attempt to understand her views about her entitlement. Mrs Wilson, as well as members of her family (especially her mother and sister) felt that she was entitled to have her bill paid by the Family Welfare Association, if not entirely, at least in part. She felt that she and her family were particularly deserving and that she was seeking help for a serious, not a frivolous reason. However she recognised that many persons came to the agency and that it was the worker's job to sift out the most needy or deserving. Mrs Wilson had eight interviews with the Family Welfare Association, with two different workers. The first worker approached matters on a practical level and initially suggested ways in which the client might economise – an attitude which the client resented. In order to increase her chances of getting help, Mrs Wilson utilised a number of 'ingratiating' techniques, several on the advice of her mother.

'Once when I was going, Mum said to me, "Take the boy with you, but don't put that coat on him – she'll think you are well off, that you are only there for the extra money." So I took her advice. I took his coat off and put his old one on. And I got help. Mum said to me another time when I was going. "Now don't be saucy, just answer her questions. Don't speak out of turn, or you won't get it." '

The second worker apparently spent more time exploring the client's family relationships, particularly her marital relationships, and she was resented even more than the first worker.

'I wouldn't have asked questions like that. She shouldn't have kept harping on it, like "How do you feel? How do you manage? How is your husband when you see him?" You don't ask questions like that, not even when you're a Welfare woman.'

Both of the caseworkers were aware of the client's views concerning her 'entitlement', but each apparently tended to discount them. According to the second worker, the client's demands of the agency derived from feelings of resentment which were connected with her husband's imprisonment.

'This electricity bill was a terrific projection of all her resentment against her husband being taken away. Her demands of the agency were symbolic of the fact that society owed her something – because society had taken her husband away. Neither of us were able to "get through" to the client. We tried to spell out to her, what payment of the electricity bill meant to her, but she grew angry every time you said it to her.'

'Her reactions gave further support to the explanations we had developed for her behaviour.' (JMB, 1981)

2. Read the following passage and answer the questions which follow.

Stigma not only affects those with a problem, who have to live with the feeling of being shameful or different, but it acts as a warning to others who might have the problem but narrowly escape or hide the fact. It also affects the reactions of other people towards the stigmatised. Various terms, such as pauper, prostitute, juvenile delinquent, call up a series of stereotypes of irresponsible people lacking in the accepted standards, collectively different and to be treated with suspicion and reserve and, in particular, having their right to maintenance in financial need put under a microscope.

Fear of being 'branded' in this way involves those in need of help in a range of emotional responses including refusal to apply for benefits and resentment and 'hostility towards a system which deliberately and continually creates the role of suppliant'.

(a) Explain the meaning of the term 'stigma' (line 1).

(b) From your studies give one example of the affects of stigma on those claiming benefits.

(c) Explain what is meant by the phrase 'a system which deliberately creates the role of suppliant' (lines 12 and 13).

(d) Give a brief account of one other explanation given by sociologists for the failure of individuals to claim the benefits to which they are entitled. (JMB, 1980)

3. We are profoundly ignorant about the ways in which the consumers of health and social services respond to the help made available to them – the consumers have rarely been asked for their opinion. Assess the importance of studying the consumers' point of view and experiences of such services. (JMB, 1981)

4. Explore, using examples, the ways in which the professions increasingly control how we understand society and ourselves. (University of London, 1983)

5. Examine the usefulness of an interactionist perspective to the understanding of client practitioner relationships. (JMB, 1981)

6. Drawing examples from any area of health and/or welfare indicate the ways in which distinctions are made between the 'deserving' and the 'undeserving'. Give a sociological explanation of why the distinction is made in such a way. (JMB, 1979)

FURTHER READING

1. L. Burghes, *Living from Hand to Mouth: A Study of 65 Families on Supplementary Benefit*, Family Service Units/Child Poverty Action Group, 1980.

   Describes the experience of poverty: the anxiety, humiliation and the careful budgeting. The book looks, too, at the reality of poverty: debt, diet, fuel, clothing, education and social life.

2. New Society Social Studies Reader, *The Origins of the Social Services*, New Society, 1983. Articles by P. Hennock, 'The Poor Law era' and 'Social security: a system emerges'.

   Surveys the development of social security from the nineteenth-century Poor Law to the reforms of the early twentieth century which culminated in the 1911 National Insurance Act.

3. New Society Social Studies Reader, *The Growth of the Social Services*, New Society, 1983. Articles by J. Harris 'From cradle to grave: the rise of the welfare state' and 'What happened after Beveridge'.

   Surveys the development of social security in the twentieth century, looking at the principles and practice of the Beveridge plan.

4. A. Deacon and J. Bradshaw, *Reserved for the Poor*, Basil Blackwell and Martin Robertson, 1983, pp. 30–46.

   Describes the changes in social policy brought about during and after the Second World War and looks at why a significant proportion of people in poverty do not claim the benefits to which they are entitled.

5. New Society Social Studies Reader, *Social Work*, New Society, 1981. Articles by S. Weir on 'What do people think about social workers?', T. Crabtree, 'The double bind of social work' and B. Jordan, 'Why social work should survive'.

   Examines public attitudes to social workers, the attitudes of social workers to their job, and the role they can play in defending the interest of the poor.

6. H. Graham and A. Oakley, 'Competing ideologies of reproduction: medical and maternal perspectives on pregnancy' in H. Roberts (ed), *Women, Health and Reproduction*, Routledge and Kegan Paul, 1981.

   Describes how doctors' and women's views of pregnancy differ, and the way in which doctors' perspectives structure doctor–patient interaction in the ante-natal clinic.

7. M. Hill, *Understanding Social Policy*, Basil Blackwell, 1980, pp. 109–56 and 137–60.

   Examines how the social security system and the personal social services are organised in Britain. Pages 109–56 describe how the social security system works, and its treatment of different types of claimant. It looks, too, at the concepts of the family, discretion and rights in social security. Pages 137–60 describe the running of the personal social services, looking at residential care and domiciliary services and the role of professional social workers and the voluntary sector.

5
Equality and efficiency in the welfare state

INTRODUCTION

The last chapter noted how social scientists usually approach the experience of poverty and ill-health through the experiences of claimants, clients and patients. This interest in professional responses to deviance is part of a wider sociological interest in how societies remain stable in time of social change. In studying Western society during the profound changes in the last 200 years, social scientists have noted that the growth of capitalism has been accompanied by a sharp increase in public expenditure on social policy. The development of collectively-funded systems of income-maintenance, education, housing and health care has been a feature of all Western societies over the last century. Their emergence has led sociologists to speculate whether these welfare systems are the means by which peaceful social change has been accomplished in the West.

Large-scale public spending on services for the people is a recent phenomenon. In the Middle Ages, public expenditure was more or less limited to military expenditure. Even in 1890, total government expenditure made up one tenth of Britain's output (Gross National Product or GNP) and nearly half of this was military and war-related spending. But over the last century, public spending has risen sharply: 10 per cent in 1890; 14 per cent in 1900; 25 per cent in 1920; 40 per cent in 1950. Today, total public expenditure accounts for 44 per cent of GNP.

Much of the growth has been due to the expansion of the welfare rather than the military budget. In 1920, the earliest date for which there are reliable data, public spending on health care, education and housing amounted to less than 3 per cent of GNP. Today, the figure is 15 per cent. In the 1980s, these three items account for over a quarter of total public spending; when social security is included, the proportion rises to well over half. The main areas of government spending are identified below.

Implicit in the expansion of welfare services is the recognition that society, through the tax system, must take some collective responsibility for the well-being of its people. It is accepted that families cannot do it all, either by buying services in the market or by providing services themselves 'for love'. However, it is

Table 5.1. Public Expenditure 1983/4

Welfare services	% of total public expenditure
Social security (benefit payments)	29
Health and personal social services	12
Education	11
Transport	4
Housing	2
Other areas of public spending	
Defence	13
Industry	5
Law and order	4
Other	20

Source: *OECD Economic Outlook*, July 1983.

often difficult to decide at what point this sharing of responsibility warrants the label 'a welfare state'. In Britain, the label is usually reserved for the period since 1945, to describe what is seen as a comprehensive range of services designed to meet all the basic needs: income, shelter, health care, education, transport.

Assessing the contribution that these welfare services have made to Western society has been a major focus within the social sciences. Two forms of assessment have become particularly popular. On the one hand, social scientists have made general assessments of the relation between the welfare state and capitalist society: here the perspective is a macro one. It is this debate which is discussed in Chapter 6. On the other hand, social scientists have looked in more specific ways at the operation of social policy and asked whether or not it has achieved its objectives. They have examined its record on the question of *social equality*: has the welfare state achieved social and economic equality through public spending? More recently, social scientists have become interested in a second objective attributed to the welfare state: that of *efficiency*. Does the welfare state distribute goods and services of high standard and at low cost? Both these criteria, of equality and efficiency, imply some point of comparison. They imply that the performance of the welfare state is being compared with some alternative system for distributing the benefits of social progress to those in need. Invariably, the point of comparison is the market. Is the welfare state better than the market?

This chapter looks at the two criteria employed in assessing the welfare state. Chapter 6 turns to consider the more general relation between the welfare state and the market-based economy of capitalism.

EQUALITY AND THE WELFARE STATE

The revenue for Britain's health and welfare services is raised in two ways; through general taxation and through National Insurance. The NHS raises nearly 90 per cent of its funds through taxes, with around 8 per cent coming from National Insurance and 3 per cent from direct charges to patients (like prescription charges). Financing the social security system is more complex. Contributory benefits, like pensions and unemployment and sickness benefits, are paid for by employed people through their National Insurance contributions. This insurance payment then covers their needs, to some extent, when they are out of work. The National Insurance fund is also used, like taxation, to finance the non-contributory system of supplementary benefit on which an increasing number of people depend for their survival.

Many people believe that this system of collective funding and collective provision has promoted equality in Britain. Surveys point to the widespread conviction that a significant redistribution of wealth has occurred, with the result that the gap beween rich and poor is smaller than it used to be (see Golding and Middleton, *Images of Welfare*, 1982). It is also generally believed that the welfare state benefits the poor more than the rich: that the poor use the services more and derive more benefit from them.

Such beliefs suggest that the idea of equality carries many different meanings. First and most fundamentally, equality can refer to *equality in health* and *equality in income*; to the fact that all individuals enjoy a similar state of health and a similar level of income. On this criteria, evidence of entrenched class differences in mortality and in earned and unearned income would suggest that the welfare state has 'failed'.

Equality can have a second, and more limited meaning, referring to the provision and use of services. The NHS, for example, sought to establish *equality of access* for all. We could therefore expect that those in similar states of ill-health would receive a similar amount and a similar standard of treatment. We could also expect that the costs of receiving health care – the costs of travel and lost earnings – would be roughly the same for everyone.

The two readings below challenge the view that the welfare state has achieved equality in either sense. The first reading looks at the data on the redistribution of income and wealth in Britain since 1945.

Reading 1

Official statistics show that over the period 1949 to 1978/9 little change occurred in the distribution of incomes. That which did occur was confined to the very richest households. The share of income enjoyed by the richest one per cent did halve over this period, from eleven per cent to $5^{1}2$ per cent. The rest of the top five per cent managed to retain most of their share . . . Overall, the top tenth of income recipients were left with a quarter of all personal incomes in 1978/9 – more than the poorest half had to share between them, and ten times as much as the poorest tenth. Inequalities in income were still therefore very substantial even in the late 1970s . . .

A similar picture emerges when we consider changes in the distribution of wealth. The most consistent long-term series of data on wealth inequalities are those prepared by A.B. Atkinson and A.J. Harrison.[1] They suggest that over the entire period 1923 to 1972, the share of wealth enjoyed by the richest one per cent declined by 0.4 per cent per year. Over that period of almost half a century, the decline in the share of the top groups was almost completely balanced by an increase in that of the slightly less well off – there was little redistribution to the poorest . . .

By the end of the 1970s one per cent of the adult population owned one quarter of all Britain's personal wealth; the top two per cent owned one third; the top five per cent owned almost half and the top 10 per cent owned almost two-thirds. Moreover, the heaviest concentrations of wealth persisted in those forms – land, company shares and government securities – which also confer on their owners social and political power. Just 400,000 people – the richest one per cent – owned almost three-quarters of the private land in Britain. A similarly small group owned almost three-quarters of the listed ordinary shares and other company securities . . .

[An] important reason for the failure of the post-war strategy of equality was that it was based on a misconception about the nature and distribution of poverty itself. In laying the foundations of the present social security system, Beveridge made the assumptions that full employment would be maintained and that poverty would be confined to those not currently participating fully in labour market activity. Hence, the social security system, as it was originally designed, explicitly excluded the 'working poor'. The 'rediscovery of poverty' in the late 1960s brought with it a realisation that a full-time job was no longer an insurance against poverty – if ever it was. The number of families rendered poor by a combination of low pay and family responsibilities has increased substantially in recent years. By 1979 the DHSS estimated that one in five of those living on an income below the official poverty line (below the supplementary benefit entitlement) were in families where there was at least one income from *full-time* employment. Next to the elderly, the working poor were then the largest single group in poverty. Many escaped poverty only through the efforts of more than one wage earner. The Central Policy Review Staff [a government think-tank, now disbanded] calculated that the numbers in poverty would quadruple were it not for the earnings of married women workers.

The low paid are most frequently in low status, insecure jobs. They are generally in poorer health and their risk of unemployment is also particularly high. Opportunities to accumulate savings, access to pension rights and the chance for home ownership are all minimal. Not only do these factors affect present standards of living, they also help to produce poverty in old age. Low wages during an individual's working life therefore have profound implications for poverty over the life cycle.

Taking account of these indirect effects, low wages may be considered the most important cause of poverty in Britain. Yet our social security system makes little provision for the working poor . . . The proliferation of means tests and the lower tax threshold have created a harsh poverty trap. By 1981, it was estimated that over 90 per cent of the families considered poor enough to claim family income supplement were paying all or part of it back in income tax. An increase in gross earnings for this group (totalling 132,000 families with children in 1981) might be wholly negated by increased tax liabiity and reduced eligibility to means-tested benefits. Once again the social security and tax system had served to reinforce, rather than to challenge, basic wage inequalities.

1. A. B. Atkinson and A. J. Harrison, *Distribution of Personal Wealth in Britain*, Cambridge University Press, 1978.

   C. Pond and J. Popay, 'Tackling inequalities at their source' in H. Glennerster (ed), *The Future of the Welfare State*, 1983, pp.104–8.

Questions
1. *Summarise, in your own words or in a diagram, the authors' evidence on the distribution of income and wealth in Britain since the Second World War.*
2. *What factors do Pond and Popay identify as responsible for the continuing inequalities in income and wealth?*
3. *What do the authors mean when they say that 'our social security system makes little provision for the working poor'?*

4. *What is the poverty trap? What measures would help eliminate it?*

The second reading is concerned with inequalities in health care. Evidence on inequalities in health was reviewed in Chapter 2, where it was suggested that health inequalities have not diminished with the provision of free medical care. The author below is concerned with whether, none the less, equality in access to health care has been achieved. Using data from the General Household Survey, Julian Le Grand found that more public money is spent on people in higher social classes who use the National Health Services. Those in social class one (professionals, managers, employers and their families) receive 40 per cent more per person in public money than those in social classes four and five (semi and unskilled manual workers and their families). His explanation of this sharp class difference is presented in the reading below.

Reading 2

Now there are two possible explanations for the inequality [in public expenditure on health care between the social classes]. The first is that it reflects the fact that the higher socio-economic groups have different diseases from the lower ones; diseases which are significantly more expensive to treat. Unfortunately, this 'fact' has little to support it . . .

The second explanation for the unequal expenditure is that there exist substantial differences in the use of the Health Service between the groups, at least in relation to their health. People in the lower SEGs appear prepared to report themselves as ill to a General Household Survey interviewer, but not to go to the doctor – or, more accurately, not to use the facilities of the Health Service to the same extent as their counterparts in the higher groups. This is borne out by a number of other studies. The National Child Development Study found that children up to the age of 7 in Social Class I, compared with those in Social Class V, were twice as likely to have visited a dentist, and five, ten and eleven times as likely to have been vaccinated against smallpox, polio and diptheria respectively . . .

The conclusion . . . [from such evidence is] that the better off appear to receive more health care under the NHS relative to need than the less well off. This also appears to have been the experience of the public health care systems of other countries. In the United States, Part B of the Medicare programme finances a large proportion of health treatment for the elderly, including all physician services, X-rays and laboratory tests, ambulance services and home health care. A study of its distribution found that those with incomes of over $15,000 per annum derived over twice as much benefit per person eligible as those with incomes under $5,000. The Medicaid programme provides free care to low-income families, and, as such, of course, largely benefits the poor as a group. But *within* that group there are substantial differences in benefit, again favouring the better off. Studies of the (very different) public health systems of Malaysia and Colombia concluded in each that public expenditure was distributed equally between income groups, a conclusion which implies that, since ill-health is almost certainly concentrated in the poorer groups, public expenditure per ill person is unequal . . .

The NHS, therefore, along with other systems of public health care, appears to favour the better off. This raises the obvious question: Why? Why do those lower down the social scale use the NHS less (relative to their need) than their middle class counterparts, even though the majority of its services are provided free? Or, put another way, why are there differences in the demand for health care between individuals in different social groups? . . .

As far as costs are concerned, there are several reasons why the costs of using a free service will be greater for potential working class users from the lower SEGs than for those from the higher ones. Time spent travelling will be greater because they are more reliant upon public transport (in 1976, under a third of semi and unskilled manual workers' households had cars compared with nearly 90 per cent of those of professionals). Also, they are likely to have further to travel, for the areas in which they live are poorly endowed with medical facilities. The costs of waiting are likely to be higher, since they cannot so easily make appointments by telephone (a quarter of unskilled manual workers' households in 1976 had telephones compared with nearly 90 per cent of those of professionals, employers and managers).

Not only may the lower groups lose more time using the NHS than the higher ones, but the cost of each hour thus lost may be greater, particularly for those in work. Many professionals and

managers are paid an annual salary and hence are unlikely to lose
income for time spent visiting the doctor during working hours,
whereas workers in manual occupations, paid by the day or the
hour, may have to forgo their pay for any time thus taken
off . . .

Not only costs but the perceptions of the benefits from health
care may differ between the groups. This may be because the
health knowledge of the lower groups is poorer in some respects
(for instance, they may know less about preventive services). But
it may also be because the benefits *are* rather less. Individuals
from lower social groups can find the Health Service – staffed as
it is with largely middle-class personnel – as at best unhelpful and
at worst actively hostile to their interests. Immigrant groups, in
particular, may encounter actual discrimination.

There is evidence to support the view that there are
considerable problems of communication between working-class
patients and doctors . . .

Costs greater, benefits lower: it is not surprising that the lower
social groups demand less medical care than the higher ones,
even when there is no charge. There is so much evidence from so
many different areas that, almost regardless of the method of
provision, the better off will always be able to make more
effective use of even a freely provided service than the less well
off. In that sense, the strategy of attempting to create equality
through the provision of services that are free, or at a subsidised
price to all, seems fundamentally misconceived. Basically, the
forces which created the inequalities in the first place and which
perpetuate them seem to be too strong to be resisted through
indirect methods such as public expenditure on the social
services. Rather, the strategy of equality has to be aimed at
tackling those forces directly.

J. Le Grand, *The Strategy of Equality*, 1982, pp. 27, 30–4, 137.

Questions
1. *How does Le Grand explain the differences in how much public
   money is spent on the health care of rich and poor in Britain?*
2. *What international evidence does he cite to support his argument? Do
   you find the argument convincing?*
3. *Why, according to Le Grand, do the costs and benefits of using a 'free'
   service vary between rich and poor?*
4. *Why does the author think the strategy of trying to create equality
   through welfare services is 'fundamentally misconceived'? What kind*

*of social policies do you think he has in mind to tackle the forces which
create inequality?*

From these two readings, the welfare state appears to have done
little to reduce income inequalities between rich and poor or to
achieve equality in their access to health care. However, it would
be wrong to conclude that it has 'failed' the poor and benefited
only the rich. When we consider all social spending, including
welfare services and cash benefits, we find that the poorest
households gain substantially while higher income households are
net losers. The welfare state also redistributes welfare in relation
to family size and stage in the life-cycle: retired households and
couples with three or more children are net gainers, receiving
more in services and benefits than they pay out in taxes. All other
households are net losers: their tax bill exceeds the costs of the
welfare services, in cash and in kind, which they consume
(Davies and Piachaud, 'Social policy and the economy', 1983).

The debate about inequality has primarily been seen in class
terms. Relatively little attention has been paid to the impact of
the welfare state on the redistribution of income between men
and women in the family, or on the equalising of access to health
care between white and black. The reading below is concerned
with the question of racial equality in the welfare state.

Reading 3

Over the past five years the NHS has changed its approach to its
black clientele. Previously black people's needs were simply
ignored and their culture dismissed as inferior. Now with black
people making more demands, their needs are being categorised
as their problem – something which is wrong with them rather
than with the NHS. To solve the problem then, black people
need to be studied . . .

But focusing attention on black people is not necessarily the
same as responding to their needs. If we look at what specific
kinds of initiatives are being taken, where resources are being
deployed, it seems that most energy and effort is going into two
kinds of things: (i) the production of books, articles and training
programmes to teach health service professionals about Asian
cultures; and (ii) health education programmes aimed at the
Asian community. Let us examine the impact of each of these.

While it is clearly important that white health service

professional workers need to be educated about the different expectations, values, and ways of doing things of other cultures, we need to look at exactly what perceptions of, and attitudes towards, black culture are being promulgated. Are racist stereotypes being challenged or reinforced? In all the books and articles we have read on Asian culture for health service professionals we have discovered much that is extremely questionable, an excessive concentration on minor practices, and, running through almost everything, a quite sickening assumption of the superiority of white middle class cultural norms . . .

Much is made for instance of the fact that Indian eye make up contains lead. The automatic assumption is that people must be stupid to go on putting this eye make up on their children. Yet everyday Western culture encourages harmful things (for instance to work with carcinogenic (cancer causing) chemicals, or to eat food containing carcinogens), and yet white people do not think of themselves as belonging to a harmful or defective culture. To feed people arbitrary 'facts' which they can incorporate within their own traditional white ways of thinking only intensifies the problem which is not 'black people' but white racism.

Another example of how black culture is regarded as an actual or potential threat is the way Hakims, practitioners of the Yunani system of medicine who provide a service to the Asian community, are portrayed. From the accounts of the health journals we get an impression of a bizarre, irrational medicine which involves harmful and dangerous practices. In fact, like acupuncture, the Yumani system of medicine is widely acknowledged to be extremely effective . . .

In each of these examples black culture is not simply being portrayed as bizarre and backward. Rather, poor health amongst black people is seen as being *caused* by the inadequacies of black culture. This is the key theme throughout the new literature on 'ethnic minorities'. . .

Although, as we made clear at the beginning of this report, higher rates of illness among black people occur because of the social and economic conditions they face, the experts are obsessed with the task of changing black people's behaviour and modifying their culture.

Brent Community Health Council, *Black People and the Health Service*, 1981, pp. 12, 13 and 16.

Questions

1. *In what ways is the NHS seen to treat its black patients?*
2. *What similarities, if any, exist between this pattern of treatment and the 'culture of poverty' model of poverty and ill-health described in Chapter 2?*
3. *What kind of changes in the NHS do you think Brent Community Health Council would advocate?*

EFFICIENCY AND THE WELFARE STATE

In assessing the performance of the welfare state, social scientists have not only examined its impact on the distribution of income and health. They have considered its economic costs as well as its social consequences. They have asked: does the welfare state provide value for money? The question of efficiency is one most frequently linked to the health service: it is the NHS, therefore, that this section considers.

Like equality, efficiency has many dimensions. Efficiency, for some, is measured by the cost of health care. These costs have risen since the NHS was established. In 1948, it was widely assumed that the demand for health care would fall as the nation became healthier. The government spoke of a 'limited quantity of morbidity' which would be reduced by medical treatment. In fact, demand has risen over time as Britain has become wealthier. It is national wealth, not national health, which has emerged as the more powerful determinant of the size of the health care budget. Part of the increase in health costs is caused by the changes in the demographic structure which Thomas McKeown identified in the reading contained in Chapter 2. As the population of the West has got richer, it has got older too. Over the last twenty years, the number of people aged 65 and over in Britain has increased by one third – by over two million people.

The problem of costs is one experienced by all Western countries. It is in this international perspective that the efficiency of the NHS is assessed. Many argue that the NHS scores well, for Britain spends a lower proportion of its GNP on health care. For others, the comparatively low cost of the NHS indicates that people in Britain are being denied both the quantity and quality of health care that they want and in other Western countries would receive. The debate about efficiency turns on whether the market is the best way of distributing scarce health resources. Those who regard the NHS as an efficient system tend to see the market as an inefficient one. It is this perspective that is presented in the reading below:

Reading 4

Should the NHS . . . be rated a success or failure? In exploring
the problems concerned in trying to answer this question, a useful
starting point is the . . . report from the Organisation for
Economic Co-operation and Development (OECD) . . . The
OECD survey confirms Britain's position as a low spender in
terms of the proportion of national income devoted to health, as
Table 5.2 shows . . .

The OECD report suggests that expenditure on health is much
like spending on consumer durables – for example, washing
machines and cars – in that it tends to rise in line with national
income. In other words, countries tend to spend a higher
proportion of their national income on health care as they get
richer: national differences appear to reflect less the relative
priority given to health care, as against other claims on national
resources, than the total wealth of the countries concerned.
Indeed, Britain's level of expenditure could roughly be predicted
simply by looking at the income per head: there's very little
wrong with the NHS, it is therefore tempting to conclude, that
could not be cured by a higher economic growth rate.

But, once again, this conclusion must be qualified. As
countries get richer, so the cost of delivering a unit of health care
or providing a given level of service appears to rise. That is, the
price of medical services tends to increase faster than prices
generally: the so-called relative price effect. In particular, in most
countries labour costs have risen sharply over the past decade,
with nursing and ancillary staff improving their position relative
to the rest of the labour force.

Consequently, therefore, the proportion of national income
spent on health may be a misleading measure of Britain's position
in the international league table in terms of actual service
provision. For example, Britain's doctors are notoriously cheaper
than in the most advanced industrial countries. The ratio of
doctor's income to per capita income is 4.5:1 in Britain, as
against 4.6 in Sweden, 6.7 in the United States, 7.0 in France,
and 8.5 in Germany. These figures confirm the position of
Britain's doctors as the proletariat of the international medical
community, and so help to explain the current state of morale.
But they also indicate that the level of care provided by the NHS
may not be as inadequate in international comparative terms as
the proportion of national income devoted to health care
suggests . . .

Interestingly, the NHS appears to be a success story even in terms of limiting expenditure on administration (Table 5.3) . . .

The comparison does seem to point to an interesting conclusion: that while the NHS may have an expensively elaborate managerial structure, it is outstandingly efficient in terms of collecting and distributing its funds. That is, it scores over other systems – like the French – because it collects its money very cheaply through the tax system, instead of working through insurance companies or funds, and does not make a multiplicity of individual charges and reimbursements. So any move towards a system based on fees, charges, or insurance seems (whatever the other merits of the case) certain to increase the number of bureaucrats and the costs of administration.

Table 5.2. Expenditure on Health as Percentage of
Gross Domestic Product (mid seventies)

	Private %	Public %	Total %
Britain	0.6	4.6	5.2
Germany	1.5	5.2	6.7
France	1.6	5.3	6.9
Sweden	0.6	6.7	7.3
United States	4.3	3.0	7.4

Table 5.3. General Administrative Costs as
Percentage of Total Expenditure

	%		%
Britain	2.6	Sweden	7.6
Germany	5.0	United States	8.8
France	10.8		

R. Klein, 'International perspectives on the NHS', *British Medical Journal*, 1977, p. 1492.

Questions

1. *How does Klein explain the data on health care spending contained in Table 5.2?*
2. *Why is the proportion of national income spent on health a misleading measure of service provision?*
3. *Why, according to Klein, does the French system of health care cost more to administer?*

A very different assessment of the efficiency of the NHS is provided in the next reading. It argues that the divorcing of service from payment, long seen as the triumph of the NHS, is in fact the cause of its failure.

Central to this body of thought, associated with the liberal economists of the nineteenth century and the monetarists of today, is the view that the market is the best way of distributing scarce resources. The market is seen to allow consumers to express their preferences through buying the kind of health care they want, direct from the suppliers. The process of buying and selling acts to limit potential excesses on both sides of the exchange. Buyers are more restrained in what they demand, having to meet the bill themselves, and sellers, no longer part of a NHS monopoly, find they must provide high quality services at competitive prices to stay in business. The market is thus seen to achieve, in terms of both cost-control and quality-control what a state monopoly can never do.

It is this perspective that the author of Reading 5 supports.

Reading 5

The welfare state . . . *first* is based on ignorance of the preferences of consumers – parents, patients, home-occupiers, pensioners – because it has no machinery for gathering information on individuals . . .

Second, ignorance provokes inefficiency. Health indicators may seem to show that the NHS does not perform worse than other more varied health systems overseas. But they measure only the measurable. They do not reflect the immeasurable elements that count with the patient: the waiting and queueing, the choice of doctor or hospital, or the timing of treatment, the responsiveness of doctors and nurses . . .

Third, the welfare state replaced choice for consumers between competing suppliers by monopoly from which there is no escape, except at a cost that the rich can bear better than the poor . . .

No wonder the welfare state is stagnant relatively to less centralised, more flexible systems of welfare where change is welcomed and rewarded. No wonder that, while the British NHS is slow to innovate in methods of organisation and financing, or even to emulate the pioneering advances in other countries, medical care in the USA displays the widest variety and the most advanced innovations in financing and organising medical service – in health maintenance organisations, pre-paid group practices, and other experimental techniques unknown in Britain because they would disturb the smooth running of the centralised NHS . . .

The higher expenditure, as a proportion of GNP, in countries with more scope for private insurance than in Britain, indicates the readiness to pay more in premiums for services that are linked more or less to the quantity or quality of medical care received than in taxes where, by definition, no such link is permitted since, as in the NHS, it would violate the principle that medical care received should bear no link with payment (by taxes) at all.

The lower figure for Britain is sometimes quoted as evidence that the NHS is more effective in avoiding waste than are other financing systems. I very much doubt that inference. Costs tend to become inflated whenever payment is by third parties outside the doctor and patient, that is, by an insurance organisation or by the state. Clearly where 'someone else' is paying, doctors and patients can indulge in conscious or unconscious collusion in a longer stay in hospital, a more renowned surgeon, a more expensive drug, an unnecessary 'frill'. But third party payment – by the state – takes place in the NHS where it is the very essence, the pride and joy, of the system. There is no comparison between the two systems.

A. Seldon, *Wither the Welfare State*, 1981, pp. 37–8, 20–2.

Questions
1. *What does the author mean when he states that the welfare state is ignorant of the preferences of consumers?*
2. *How would Arthur Seldon interpret the data in Tables 5.2 and 5.3?*
3. *Why does the author maintain that the NHS is likely to be wasteful?*

The two passages, by Klein and Seldon, address the question of efficiency in terms of how the service is delivered. Other social scientists have approached the question of efficiency rather differently. They are concerned less with the *system* of medical care than with the *content* of medical care. Their focus is on the nature of Western medicine, whether delivered through the market or the state. Klein's analysis, like the passage by McKeown in Chapter 2, suggests that an increasing demand for health care is the result of improved health and greater wealth; it is not the cause of better health. Taken one stage further, this argument suggests that medicine may create its own demand. Moreover, the demand that medicine creates may be for inappropriate remedies, remedies which it can supply but which do not alleviate suffering. Western medicine is thus inefficient because it is ultimately ineffective.

This argument is advanced in different ways, and with different conclusions, by a variety of social scientists. One influential current is represented by writers like Ivan Illich and Ian Kennedy. In their view, 'the medicalisation of life' has increased our dependence on professionals who see the body as a sick engine and themselves as mechanics (see Chapter 1, on the medical model). While doctors should be adopting a different and more modest role in the care of the old and chronic sick, they are building on their image as high-technology specialists with 'a pill for every ill'.

Reading 6

The diseases afflicting Western societies have undergone dramatic changes. In the course of a century, so many mass killers have vanished that two-thirds of all deaths are now associated with the diseases of old age. Those who die young, are more often than not victims of accidents, violence and suicide.

These changes in health status are generally equated with progress and are attributed to more or better medical care. In fact, there is no evidence of any direct relation between this mutation [change in the pattern] of sickness and the so-called progress of medicine . . .

(1) *Doctor's Effectiveness – An Illusion*
The study of the evolution of disease patterns provides evidence that during the last century doctors have affected such patterns no more profoundly than did priests during earlier times . . . Discussion on the future of health care might usefully begin with this recognition . . .

The fact that there are more doctors where certain diseases have become rare has little to do with their ability to control or eliminate them. It simply means that doctors deploy themselves as they like, more so than other professionals, and that they tend to gather where the climate is healthy, where the water is clean, and where people work and can pay for their services.

(2) *Useless Medical Treatment*
Awe-inspiring medical technology has combined with egalitarian rhetoric to create the dangerous delusion that contemporary medicine is highly effective.

During the last generation, a limited number of specific procedures have indeed become effective. Those which are applicable to widespread diseases are usually very inexpensive: unless they are monopolized for personal use, they require a minimum of personal skills, materials or hotel services from hospitals. In contrast, most of the skyrocketing medical expenditures are destined for diagnosis and treatment of no or of doubtful effectiveness . . .

(3) *Doctor-inflicted Injuries*

The impact of medicine constitutes one of the most rapidly expanding epidemics of our time. The pain, dysfunction, disability and even anguish which result from technical medical intervention now rival the morbidity due to traffic, work and even war-related activities. Only modern malnutrition is clearly ahead.

The technical term for the new epidemic of doctor-made disease, Iatrogenesis, is composed of the Greek words for 'physician' (iatros) and for 'origins' (genesis). Iatrogenic disease comprises only illness which would not have come about unless sound and professionally recommended treatment had been applied . . .

Medicines have always been potentially poisonous, but their unwanted side-effects have increased with their effectiveness and widespread use. Every 24 to 36 hours, from 50% to 80% of adults in the U.S. and the U.K. swallow a medically prescribed chemical . . .Some drugs are addictive, others mutilating, others mutagenic, although perhaps only in synergy [combination] with food colouring or insecticide. In some patients, antibiotics alter the normal bacterial flora and induce a super-infection, permitting more resistant organisms to proliferate and invade the host. Other drugs contribute to the breeding of drug-resistant strains of bacteria. Unnecessary surgery is a standard procedure. Disabling non-diseases result from the medical treatment of non-existent diseases. . .

(4) *Defenceless Patients*

Medical practice sponsors sickness by reinforcing a morbid society that not only preserves its defectives, but also exponentially breeds demand for the patient role. On the one hand defectives survive in increasing numbers and are fit only for life under institutional care, while on the other hand, medically

certified symptoms exempt people from destructive wage-labour
and excuse them from the struggle to reshape the society in which
they live . . .

The so-called health professions have an even deeper,
structurally health-denying effect insofar as they destroy the
potential of people to deal with their human weakness,
vulnerability and uniqueness in a personal and autonomous
way . . .

[This form of] *iatrogenesis* consists in the paralysis of healthy
responses to suffering. It strikes when people accept health
management designed on the engineering model, when they
conspire in an attempt to produce something called 'better
health' which inevitably results in the managed maintenance of
life on high levels of sub-lethal illness.

I. Illich, *Medical Nemesis*, 1975, pp. 15–26.

Questions
1. *How does Illich see the role of medicine in Western society?*
2. *According to Illich, how does medicine create the illusion that it is highly effective?*
3. *What does Illich mean by iatrogenesis? How do you think people could resist 'the paralysis of healthy responses to suffering'?*

ESSAY QUESTIONS

1. It is often assumed that social security, along with other sectors of the welfare state, is instrumental in the redistribution of wealth from rich to poor and operates mainly to the benefit of lower income groups. Assess the validity of this assumption in the light of sociological evidence. (JMB, 1980)

2. Using evidence from your studies, examine the nature and extent of the inequalities which exist in the field of health. (JMB, 1981)

3. 'In Britain now the richest one per cent still owns one fifth and perhaps as much as one quarter of all personal wealth. Income is less unequally distributed, but here again recent official estimates show that, in 1974–5, the richest one per cent took home about the same amount as the poorest twenty per cent' (Halsey, *Change in British Society*). Examine the different ways in which sociologists have explained these inequalities in income and wealth. (AEB, 1982)

4. 'Social Services . . . do little to equalise the distribution of rewards flowing from the institutions of market, private property and inheritance' (Mishra, *Society and Social Policy*). Explain and discuss. (AEB, 1982)

5. 'The availability of good medical care tends to vary inversely with the needs of the population served.' Discuss. (AEB, 1982)

6. 'The welfare state has ensured for everyone a basic minimum level of subsistence, but it has not led to any fundamental transformation of British society.' Discuss. (Oxford Local Examination, 1982)

7. What explanations can sociologists offer for the persistence of poverty into the 1980s? How adequate are these explanations? (JMB, 1982)

FURTHER READING

1. M. Hill, *Understanding Social Policy*, Basil Blackwell and Martin Robertson, 1980, pp. 161–79.

   Describes the organisation of the NHS. It looks at the problems of resource-distribution between hospital and community care, of equality of treatment and of rationing.

2. D. Widgery, *Health in Danger: The Crisis in the Health Service*, Macmillan, 1979, pp. 33–60.

   Examines the problems facing the NHS today: the causes of ill-health which lie beyond its boundaries, the shortage of cash and new hospitals, and the dominance of the medical profession.

3. R. Maxwell, *Health and Wealth: An International Study of Health-Care Spending*, Lexington Books, 1981, pp. 34–40, 100–9.

   Looks at the international evidence on spending on medical care, to assess the performance of the NHS.

4. New Society Social Studies Reader, *The Growth of the Social Services*, New Society, 1983. Articles by A. Briggs on 'Making health every citizen's birthright' and 'The achievements, failures and aspirations of the NHS'.

   Looks at the development of state health care from the Poor Law to 1948, when the NHS began. Describes the problems the NHS has experienced since then and the measures introduced in response to them.

5. Unit for the Study of Health Policy, *The NHS in the Next 30 Years: A New Perspective on the Health of the British*, Department of Community Medicine, Guy's Hospital Medical School, pp. 5–20.

   Describes the NHS in the current context of Britain's economic decline and demographic change. It examines the changing patterns and causes of mortality in Britain, and the international trends in health care spending.

6
The welfare state: care or control

INTRODUCTION

This chapter examines the wider debate about the welfare state, a debate concerned with the relation between social policy and the capitalist economy. This debate is a complex and confusing one which extends beyond the boundaries of sociology, into economics, history and politics. Participants to the debate tend to adopt their own particular vocabulary to describe what they see as the crucial features of capitalism and welfare. 'Breaking the code' of the various theories can sometimes be difficult, but keep trying!

Controversy has surrounded the question of state intervention since it developed on a significant scale in the nineteenth century. In 1846, *The Economist* ran an editorial warning of 'the general helplessness of the masses, which is sure to be induced by the state undertaking to provide for their welfare. They come to rely on it and take no care for themselves. They trust in it and become its dependents.' More than 130 years later we find similar views still being expressed. Rhodes Boyson in *Down With The Poor* (1971), for example, argues that 'the normal fibre of our people has been weakened. A state which does for its citizens what they can do for themselves is an evil state . . . In such an irresponsible society no-one cares, no-one saves, no-one bothers – why should they when the state spends all its energies taking money from the energetic, successful and thrifty to give to the idle, the failures and the feckless?'

While the welfare state has developed against a backcloth of controversy, there have been periods when disagreement has been more muted. Particularly during the thirty-year period from the 1940s to the early 1970s, there was a wider political consensus about the need for a welfare state. A commitment to welfare was seen as part of a package of changes introduced in the aftermath of the Second World War to ensure that Britain never again experienced the unemployment and poverty of the 1930s. The existence of the welfare state was not a party issue; all the major political parties were 'for' it, although, in different ways, they remained critical of its performance.

Since the 1970s, this consensus has broken down. No longer is it accepted that the welfare state is the best way of providing for the needy and promoting a fairer and more equal society. Social scientists have been an important source of ideas, providing perspectives which both challenge and defend the need for a welfare state.

Four major positions are considered in this chapter. Labelling, as we know from earlier chapters, tends to oversimplify and distort reality. None the less, the labels do represent important lines of division within the social sciences.

The oldest and most influential tradition is that of *market liberalism* (not to be confused with the philosophy of today's Liberal Party). *Market liberals*, or *monetarists* as they are now called, view capitalism favourably. When run on *laissez-faire* (letting alone) lines, the market is seen to promote both individual well-being and 'the common weal' (social welfare). A welfare state, except of the most basic kind, is therefore considered unnecessary, interfering with the market and the spirit of responsibility it encourages in buyers and sellers. A second tradition of *conflict theories* makes a very different evaluation of capitalism, seeing it as creating a deeply divided and unstable society. Welfare policies are introduced reluctantly by the powerful to deal with these problems of social conflict and instability, providing services in such a way that social unrest is diffused, but the inequalities which underlie it are maintained. The label *conflict theories* encompasses a wide range of perspectives. Singled out in this chapter are *Marxist theories*, which trace inequality and conflict back to the class structure, and *feminist theories*, which link inequality and conflict not only to class divisions but to the social divisions between men and women. In both accounts, the welfare state, far from jeopardising the work of capitalists as the liberals claim, is seen as part of an infrastructure necessary for capitalism to survive. Finally, there is the *social democratic tradition* associated with Richard Titmuss, R.H. Tawney and T.H. Marshall. Like the Marxist and feminist traditions, this perspective is highly critical of the market system, which distributes economic rewards according to the ability to pay. However, it sees the welfare state as introducing a very different system of distribution, based on need not wealth. The welfare state can thus establish a new moral order in Britain, based on altruistic giving through the tax system. This perspective emphasises the possibility of consensus emerging through collectively-provided services.

While these perspectives provide very different assessments of the welfare state, there are some points of agreement. These are worth noting before we examine the traditions in more detail.

First, there is general agreement about the term 'the welfare state'. For most people, the welfare state refers to the government-operated social services: social security (national insurance, supplementary benefit, child benefit and so on), health care, personal social services (principally social work and probation), education, housing and public transport. Generally excluded are the other items of public expenditure (defence, industry, roads and the police) and government management of the economy (by pay norms, tax levels and so on). The main areas of welfare spending were identified in Chapter 5 (Table 5.1).

Secondly, most social scientists agree that the welfare state has not achieved social equality. The data presented in Chapter 5, indicating the continuing inequalities in income and wealth, in health and access to health care, are generally accepted by all three traditions.

Thirdly, in seeking to understand why inequality has survived, social scientists agree that they need to begin with an analysis of capitalism, for it is acknowledged that it was in the context of the capitalist economy that the welfare state developed. The initial attempts at government welfare provisions were prompted by the need to cope with the casualties of the new economic order. These initial attempts, culminating in the 1834 Poor Law, are seen to have supported the emerging capitalist order (but not necessarily the poor). Since 1834, and particularly since 1945, welfare policies are seen to have taken a different direction. Increased in size and scope, the welfare state now stands as an alternative to the market, providing a comprehensive range of services in education, health, housing and transport for all who choose or need to use them. While agreement exists on the questions of the definition of the welfare state and the context of its development, it extends no further.

LIBERAL PERSPECTIVES

The liberal model rests on an analysis of individual behaviour, and in particular, of the kind of choices individuals make when free to do so. The market is seen as the place in which choice is maximised, with individuals entering as buyers and sellers. The market, in maximising choice and freedom, is seen as morally preferable to the alternative systems for exchanging goods and services, like, for example, the nationalised industries of gas and electricity and the welfare state. The market is also seen as more efficient than systems where production is organised collectively and consumers do not pay directly for the goods they receive. Since 'collectivism' is seen to encourage waste and irresponsibility, market liberals argue that the welfare state should not have been invented. 'Most of the present welfare programmes should never have been enacted. If they had not been, many of the people now dependent on them would have become self-reliant individuals instead of wards of state. In the short run, that might have appeared cruel for some, leaving them no option to low-paying, unattractive work. But in the long run, it would have been far more humane' (Friedman and Friedman, *Free to Choose*, 1980, p. 119).

As this comment indicates, individuals in the liberal model are invariably identified as people with jobs or people for whom jobs, albeit low paid ones, are available. There is less mention of the old, the young and the unemployed, who are unable to get a share of income through the market. Where social hierarchies are recognised, they are the hierarchies of income and wealth created by 'chance and choice'. 'Chance determines our genes and through them our mental and physical capacities. Chance determines the kind of family and cultural environment into which we are born . . . Choice also plays an important role: our decisions about how to use our resources, whether to work hard or take it easy, to enter one occupation or another, to save or to spend . . . ' (*Free to Choose*, p. 22).

The market liberals advocate help for those outside the labour market provided that it does not infringe the freedom of those who give: 'private charity directed at helping the less fortunate is an example of the proper use of freedom' (Friedman, *Capitalism and Freedom*, 1962, p. 195). Such help should not undermine the incentive to work: tax-funded welfare services (like health care and social security) which maintain dependants on incomes comparable with those enjoyed by wage-earners are regarded as incompatible with the principles of freedom and self-help. As Friedman acknowledges, the pursuit of individual freedom and social justice are ultimately incompatible: 'equality comes sharply into conflict with freedom; one must choose. One cannot be an egalitarian and a liberal' (*Capitalism and Freedom*, p. 195).

The first and most influential of the market liberals was Adam Smith (1973–90). His book, *Inquiry into the Nature and Causes of the Wealth of Nations*, published in 1776, laid out its economic principles, while John Stuart Mill outlined its basic social philosophy in *Principles of Political Economy*, published in 1848. Today, market liberals have found inspiration in the work of two economists, Milton Friedman and F.A. Hayek. It is the first of these writers who provides the reading below.

Reading 1

[The major theme of this book] is the role of competitive capitalism – the organisation of the bulk of economic activity through private enterprise operating in a free market – as a system of economic freedom and political freedom . . . It is extremely convenient to have a label for the political and economic viewpoint elaborated in this book. The rightful and proper label is liberalism . . . As it developed in the late eighteenth and early nineteenth century, the intellectual movement that went under the name of liberalism emphasised freedom as the ultimate goal and the individual as the ultimate entity of the society. It supported laissez faire as a means of reducing the role of the state in economic affairs and thereby enlarging the role of the individual . . . The characteristic feature of action through political channels (by governments) is that it tends to require or enforce substantial conformity. The great advantage of the market, on the other hand, is that it permits wide diversity. It is, in political terms, a system of proportional representation. Each man can vote, as it were, for the color of tie he wants and get it; he does not have to see what color the majority want and then, if he is in the minority, submit. It is this feature of the market that we refer to when we say that the market provides economic freedom. But this characteristic also has implications that go far beyond the narrowly economic . . . The heart of the liberal philosophy is a belief in the dignity of the individual in his freedom to make the most of his capacities and opportunities subject only to the proviso that he does not interfere with the freedom of other individuals to do the same. Government action can never duplicate the variety and diversity of individual action. At any moment in time, by imposing uniform standards in housing, or nutrition, or clothing, government could undoubtedly improve the level of living of many individuals . . . But in the process, government would replace progress by stagnation, it would substitute uniform mediocrity for variety . . .

M. Friedman, *Capitalism and Freedom*, 1962, pp. 4–5, 15, 194 and 195.

Questions
1. *How does the author define liberalism?*
2. *What is meant by economic freedom? How does the market provide economic freedom?*
3. *Why is the author against state intervention to improve people's standard of living? Do you think he is right?*

CONFLICT THEORISTS

The picture of capitalism contained in the writings of conflict theories stands in sharp contrast to that painted by liberal theories. Interestingly, however, conflict theorists share with Friedman a deep distrust of the welfare state. For Marxist theorists, distrust springs from the role that the state is seen to play in the maintenance of the class structure; for feminist theorists, distrust springs from its perceived role in the mainten-ance of the sex role system.

Marxist theories

While market liberals see the world in terms of individuals, Marxist theorists see it in terms of economic systems and social groups. Britain's economic system, capitalism, is seen to create social groups who are antagonistic to each other. The market is no longer the setting in which all individuals exercise choice, but one in which some groups exercise power. Power rests in controlling the production process, ensuring that the nature of the work and the hierarchies in the workplace leave the worker as only 'a cog in the wheel'. In such a system, conflict is regarded as inevitable. According to Victor George 'the model of the social system is one of conflict of interests rather than consensus of values and interests between the two vaguely defined groups in society, the working class which includes the poor and the upper class which includes the ruling class' (George, *Social Security and Society*, 1973, p. 2).

It is in the context of class conflict that the welfare state is set. It is viewed as a peace-keeping mechanism, a way of reconciling workers to the existing regime. The welfare state is seen therefore as a victory for neither the working class nor the ruling class. It is a compromise solution in which there are gains and losses on both sides.

For capitalists, government intervention in the market is tolerated because increased welfare spending provides them with a fitter and a more docile workforce. There is historical evidence to suggest that politicians were not unaware of these benefits of welfare spending. Thus Bismarck, who engineered Germany's social insurance scheme in the 1880s, noted that 'one who can look forward to an old age pension is far more contented and much easier to manage'. A generation later in England, in 1919, Lloyd George sold the idea of council housing to his Cabinet as an insurance against the kind of revolution which had recently occurred in Russia. He warned that 'we had promised them reforms time and time again, but had done little. We must give them the conviction this time that we meant it . . . Even if it cost a hundred million pounds, what was that compared with the stability of the state?' (quoted in Swenarton, *Homes Fit for Heroes*, 1981, p. 78). While providing benefits to capitalists, the welfare state is seen also to impose a financial burden, a burden which is increasing sharply in the present day.

For the working class, the welfare state similarly offers benefits, but only at a cost. It benefits working people by the resources it provides (housing, health care and an income in times of need), resources for which working-class people have campaigned over the last 100 years. Working-class pressure was exerted through trade unions and the labour movement, as well as through the rapid growth of workers' parties, like the Labour Party, which drew their electoral support from working-class people. While political pressure secured improvements in living conditions, Marxist theorists identify losses as well as gains. Vital services are provided, but in such a way as to isolate and stigmatise the recipients of welfare and prevent them joining with the working class in collective action.

The complex process through which the welfare state has evolved is reviewed in the passage beneath.

Reading 2

Perspectives which suggest that the welfare state is an oasis of socialism mistakenly imply that the working class has been the prime mover in not only prompting welfare reform, but in shaping and administering it. It is true that the support of the organised working class has been crucial to almost all progressive reforms, but one cannot argue that the welfare state is the product of a consistent mass campaign by the working-class movement. The labour movement has never, in fact, developed and promoted a programme of State Welfare measures . . .

While the working class has exerted little 'real' control over welfare policy and administration, it is equally true that the welfare state is a response to the presence of the working class, and the continuing plight of either some or all of its members' inadequate or insecure living conditions. This presence comes to the attention of governments and the bourgeoisie in any number of ways, apart from Labour movement pressure and pressure from other groups.

Important examples in Britain might include the cholera epidemics of the mid-nineteenth century, the West End riots of the 1880s, the strikes and revolutionary agitation before and after the First World War, the hunger marches and rent strikes of the inter-war period, unofficial strikes in the 1960s, delinquency, squatting, family breakdown and so on. While none of these phenomena have represented an organised threat to the state, they forcibly bring home to the bourgeoisie the existence of a class or fragments of it which either rejects or is rejected by bourgeois values and whose needs must to some extent be accommodated or repressed to ensure the survival of capi-talism . . .

In the end, of course, the working class has had to accept capitalist welfare as an immediate amelioration [improvement] of its conditions of existence, though it has resisted the terms on which it has been offered, and opposed means-testing, work relief and fair rents, etc. But this acceptance has been predicated on the hope that the working class would be able to impose its own values on the welfare state through Parliamentary channels . . .

One may argue that state welfare represents a *quid pro quo* or a 'bribe' offered to the working class in exchange for political quiescence and industrial peace. This was certainly Bismarck's view of his social insurance schemes, Lenin's view of Lloyd George's welfare legislation and a common interpretation of the reforms initiated by the Beveridge report. It captures the political importance of capitalist state welfare, which is correctly considered by working-class consumers as a 'piece of the cake' sacrificed by capital to secure their wider cooperation. The Welfare State indeed exerts an important cushioning effect on working-class experience, actively diverting attention from the structure of class inequality.

N. Ginsberg, *Class, Capital and Social Policy*, 1979, pp. 7, 10–12.

Questions

1. *What role does the author think the working class played in the development of the welfare state?*
2. *Why did working-class people accept welfare services based on means testing?*
3. *What does the author mean when he says the welfare state is a bribe? Do you agree with him?*

Marxist theories focus on the way in which state intervention in the market has ensured both the health of the workforce and their commitment to the market system. The welfare state, in other words, maintains the social order necessary for capitalism to survive. This social order is seen primarily as the class structure: it is class inequality which the welfare state perpetuates. Recently, writers on social policy have begun to look at the role of the welfare state and the market economy in sustaining the social divisions of race, age and sex. The issue of sex inequality has received particular attention.

Feminist theories

Most sociologists now recognise that capitalism rests not only a class hierarchy but on a gender hierarchy as well. Women and men play different roles, typically in different places and with different rewards. Women tend to perform the unpaid caring roles: they socialise children and look after husbands and elderly relatives, they arrange visits to the doctor and welcome the health visitor and social worker. Women tend to do the paid caring work as well: as catering and laundry workers, as nurses and teachers, social workers and home helps. Meanwhile, men's work tends to involve the making and selling of things, rather than the making and repairing of people. Their work is not only different, it tends to be better paid and to provide them with ways of reaching the centres of political and economic influence.

The organisation of these sex roles is seen to reflect not so much innate differences in the temperaments of women and men as socially-created differences in their access to scarce resources; to education and scientific training, for example, and to housing and welfare benefits. Because of these differences in access, women are more likely than men to find themselves economically dependent on others for the money they need to survive. They are, as a result, more likely to be poor. They are also more likely to be in poor health.

Their higher risk of economic dependency and poverty and of ill-health (but not premature death) makes the welfare state of particular importance to women. For example, women constitute two-thirds of the elderly and two-thirds of the physically handicapped population and over half of the families on social security are female-headed one-parent families.

Despite their greater reliance on the welfare state, feminists argue that women have long been received on unequal terms to men. Welfare legislation has historically been concerned, like the wider economy, with workers, and with male workers in particular. Women, it is suggested, feature as dependants, whose unpaid work in the home is supported by the wages of their husbands or fathers. The 1834 Poor Law Act, for example, was primarily concerned with able-bodied men and encouraging them to maintain their families through paid work (unsupported women, like the aged, were admitted to the workhouse). The 1911 National Insurance Act insured male workers; married women and children were not covered and had to find other ways of meeting their medical bills. It was thus not until the coming of the NHS in 1948 that the insurance principle was extended to include non-working women. However, the Beveridge Report, with its network of welfare and benefit schemes, is seen still to work on a traditional model of the family in which men were breadwinners and women were their non-employed housewives.

Today, 60 per cent of married women have paid jobs. Yet feminist sociologists suggest that the basic thinking behind the Beveridge scheme remains unchanged. This is the argument developed in the reading below, which is concerned with the position of women in today's social security system.

Reading 3

The origins of the social security system and the circumstances of
the majority of its beneficiaries provide little justification for the
automatic definition of man as paid worker, women as full-time
housewife . . . For example, Rowntree (1922) in his first study of
poverty in York at the end of the nineteenth century decided to
classify families according to family income rather than by the
wages of the male earner because the wages of wives and children
'frequently amount to *more* than the earnings of the head' (p. 56,
my italics).

However, the first national insurance scheme started by Lloyd
George in 1911 copied the Friendly societies whose membership
was drawn mainly from the more skilled and regularly employed
sections of the labour force. Their normal practice was based on
the concept of the male breadwinner, paying benefits to the sick
or injured man but excluding benefits for his wife and family.

Thirty years later, Beveridge revised and extended the national
insurance scheme to all income groups in his report which forms
the basis of much of the post-war social security legislation. The
expanded scheme was still firmly based on the assumption that
marriage permanently removed women from the labour market.
Housewives were treated as a special class, a dependent class,
and were given the choice of not paying full contributions, relying
instead on their husbands, each of whom contributed (Beveridge
Report, 1942, p. 50) 'on behalf of himself and his wife, as for a
team'. Ignoring the not inconsiderable evidence that neither
women themselves, nor the economic policy-makers, regarded
women's war-time employment as a temporary measure,
Beveridge states (1942, p. 50) 'the attitude of the housewife to
gainful employment outside the home is not and should not be
the same as that of a single woman. She has other duties.'

The Social Security Pensions Act 1975 . . . removes some of
the inequalities which married women have experienced in the
social insurance system for over half a century. However, the
concept of female dependency has not been weakened . . .

It is clear then that the social security system like the tax
system only supports men and women in specific roles. Even role
sharing, not to mention role reversal, often results in heavier
taxation or reduces entitlement to social security benefits.
Throughout both systems the assumption is that women become
dependent on men once they marry or cohabit: breadwinners are

male and only women have responsibilities for domestic work. Reading the social security legislation it would be difficult to deduce that in 1971, one in six households (excluding pensioner households) relied on a woman's income for support and that the majority of these households contained dependants. It would also be hard to realise that the 'typical' family consisting of man in full-time employment, woman full-time housewife and two dependent children, is at any point in time a *minority* of families (about 10 per cent in 1971) . . .

Why then, do the state's income-maintenance schemes still only support men in the role of chief breadwinner and woman as man's dependent housewife? The answer must lie in the fact that there are enormous advantages to the economically powerful groups in our society in sustaining the belief that men are breadwinners and women, at most, are supplementary earners, whose primary duties lie in the home. In this way work incentives for men are preserved even among low-wage earners whose wives also have to work to support the family. At the same time it justifies paying women lower wages than men. Women when they enter the labour market do so in the belief that they do not need as high a wage as a man. Moreover, their paid employment must take second place to their unpaid work in the home. They, therefore, form a very cheap, docile and flexible section of the labour force and the majority confine themselves to the less secure and less rewarding jobs. At the same time they continue to care for husbands, children, the elderly and the infirm at a minimum cost to the state. However, it should not be forgotten, of course, that when we talk of economic advantage, we have, as Eleanor Rathbone pointed out forty years ago 'an economic structure devised by and for men'.

> H. Land, 'Sex role stereotyping in the social security and income tax systems' in J. Chetwynd and O. Hartnett (eds), *The Sex Role System*, 1978, pp. 137–8, 140 and 142.

Questions
1. *What does the author mean by 'female dependency'?*
2. *In what ways does the social security system treat women and men differently?*
3. *How does the author explain these differences? Do you think she is right?*

SOCIAL DEMOCRATIC THEORISTS

Like liberal and conflict theorists, the social democratic theorists recognise that capitalism is based on the market in which individuals have the right to acquire private property and personal wealth through buying and selling. Social democratic theorists share with conflict theorists the view that this market system is inherently unjust. They argue that the market does not and cannot provide a reasonable income for dependent groups. The free market system therefore cannot abolish poverty, and economic growth alone cannot create prosperity for all.

While deeply critical of the market system, social democratic theorists have a different perspective to conflict theorists on the welfare state. They acknowledge that much of the welfare state is but a pale reflection of the market economy it seeks to support. However, some of its policies contain the beginning of a new moral order which can heal the deep divides of class, race and sex. The new moral order is based on altruism, not self-interest; on a sense of concern and responsibility for others in the community. It is realised through a non-market system of distribution, based on collectively-provided services to which all have access. It is these universal services, provided through taxes, which are seen as the key to fostering a new moral commitment to welfare-for-all. Through a welfare state based on the principle of universalism, the market can be tamed and controlled, and a new socialist economic order introduced peacefully in the place of capitalism.

Richard Titmuss is regarded as the major proponent of this optimistic reading of the welfare state. The reading below is drawn from two of his major works.

Reading 4

Consider, first, the nature of the broad principles which helped to shape substantial sections of British welfare legislation in the past, and particularly the principle of universalism embodied in such post-war enactments as the National Health Service Act, the Education Act of 1944, the National Insurance Act and the Family Allowances Act.

One fundamental historical reason for the adoption of this [universal] principle was the aim of making services available and accessible to the whole population in such ways as would not involve users in any humiliating loss of status, dignity or self-respect. There should be no sense of inferiority, pauperism, sham or stigma in the use of a publicly provided service: no attribution that one was being or becoming a 'public burden'. Hence the emphasis on the social rights of all citizens to use or not to use as responsible people the services made available by the community in respect of certain needs which the private market and the family were unable or unwilling to provide universally. If these services were not provided for everybody by everybody they would either not be available at all, or only for those who could afford them, and for others on such terms as would involve the infliction of a sense of inferiority and stigma.

Avoidance of stigma was not, of course, the only reason for the development of the twin-concepts of social rights and universalism. Many other forces, social, political and psychological, during a century and more of turmoil, revolution, war and change, contributed to the clarification and acceptance of these notions . . . The emphasis today on 'welfare' and the 'benefits of welfare' often tends to obscure the fundamental fact that for many consumers the services used are not essentially benefits or increments to welfare at all; they represent partial compensations for disservices, for social costs and social insecurities which are the product of a rapidly changing industrial-urban society. They are part of the price we pay to some people for bearing part of the costs of other people's progress; the obsolescence of skills, redundancies, premature retirements, accidents, many categories of disease and handicap, urban blight and slum clearance, smoke pollution and a hundred-and-one other socially generated disservices. They are the socially caused diswelfares; the losses involved in aggregate welfare gains.

We have, as societies, to make choices; either to provide social services, or to allow the social costs of the system to lie where they fall. The nineteenth century chose the latter – the *laissez faire* solution. What we suggest is that the ways in which society organises and structures its social institutions – and particularly its health and welfare institutions – can encourage or discourage the altruistic in man; such systems can foster integration or alienation; they can allow . . . generosity towards strangers to spread among and between social groups and generations. This, we further suggest, is an aspect of freedom in the twentieth century which, compared with the emphasis on consumer choice in material acquisitiveness, is insufficiently recognised. It is indeed little understood how modern society, technical, professional, large scale organised society, allows few opportunities for ordinary folk to articulate giving in morally practical terms outside their own network of family and personal relationships.

R. Titmuss, *Commitment to Welfare*, 1968, pp. 129 and 133, and
The Gift Relationship, 1970, pp. 225–6.

Questions

1. *What is meant by universalism? What reasons does the author give for the development of universal services such as the National Health Service?*

2. *What is meant by 'socially caused diswelfares'? In the author's opinion, what responsibility do societies have to those who experience diswelfare?*

3. *In what ways can the organisation of health and welfare services encourage altruism? How could altruism be further encouraged through Britain's welfare state?*

4. *Do you agree with Titmuss's view that universal welfare services 'can allow generosity towards strangers to spread'?*

===

ESSAY QUESTIONS

1. Read the passage and answer the questions which follow.

   Social policy does not evolve out of humanitarianism or compassion but as a response by ruling elites to threats to social stability. Social control and the affirmation of the work ethic are its main objectives. Ruling elites are said to act on the basis of certain predictable patterns of behaviour, to defend their self-interest and to assert their superiority. Beginning with the sixteenth century, on a number of occasions poor relief might be said to have expanded as a response to violence or threats of violence. Social policy, then, has been seen by some writers as a long-term strategy to divert the energies of the working class from revolutionary pursuits.

   Similarly, in contemporary social welfare agencies, welfare professionals, claiming expert knowledge to diagnose individual deficiencies and provide the correct treatment, whatever their good intentions, help to maintain the power of the ruling elite. Anyone, whether social worker, educator or physician engaging in an activity to modify or set boundaries on human conduct, is engaging in social control, which takes three forms: socialisation, direct behaviour control and re-socialisation.

   (a) Illustrate how the activities of any one welfare professional may involve social control in the form of (i) direct behaviour control; (ii) re-socialisation. (You may use the same welfare professional to illustrate (i) and (ii).)

   (b) Briefly outline an alternative view of the function of social welfare to the one outlined in the passage. (JMB, 1982).

2. Why do industrial societies have welfare state systems? (AEB, 1982).

3. 'The role of the welfare state is to maintain existing levels of social inequality in a legitimated form.' Discuss. (AEB, 1983).

4. Examine the view that the welfare state treats men and women as different and unequal.

5. It has been claimed that 'the strongest influence in the development of the welfare state has been the successful attempt of the dominant social groups to buttress the existing social and economic order.' What do you understand by this claim? To what extent do you think it adequately accounts for the development of welfare provision? (JMB, 1983)

6. 'Marxism is little more than simplistic economic determinism.' Discuss with particular reference to at least *one* area of investigation. (University of London, 1982)

FURTHER READING

1. G. Room, *The Sociology of Welfare*, Basil Blackwell and Martin Robertson, 1979, pp. 41–66.

Describe a range of different perspectives on the welfare state: Marxist, liberal and social democratic.

2. R. Mishra, *The Welfare State in Crisis*, Wheatsheaf Books, 1984, pp. 26–100 and 121–60.

Like Room's book, this describes and evaluates Marxist, liberal and social democratic perspectives on the welfare state.

3. N. Bosanquet, *After the New Right*, Heinemann, pp. 5–25.

Looks at the main principles which underlie liberal perspectives on capitalism and the welfare state: that inequality is inevitable, that capitalism promotes freedom and prosperity for all and that the welfare state has failed to meet its objectives.

4. D. Frazer, *The Evolution of the Welfare State*, Macmillan, 1973, pp. 91–114.

Describes the historical development of liberal ideas, examining the work of Adam Smith, John Stuart Mill and Samuel Smiles, and the ideas of those who opposed the liberal doctrine on welfare in the nineteenth century.

5. J. Coussins and A. Coote, *The Family in the Firing Line: A Discussion Document on Family Policy*, National Council for Civil Liberties/Child Poverty Action Group, 1981.

Examines why governments are interested in 'the family' in the context of recent changes in family life. It looks at the concept of 'the family wage' and its impact on wage and benefit levels and argues for a feminist approach to family policy.

6. E. Wilson, *Women and the Welfare State*, Tavistock, 1977, pp. 73–97.

Describes the kind of attitudes to women, motherhood and the family that were built into the welfare state after the Second World War.

7. R. Titmuss, 'Welfare state and welfare society' in E. Butterworth and R. Holman (eds), *Social Welfare in Modern Britain*, Fontana, 1975, pp. 25–37.

Contains Titmuss's social democratic views on the need for the welfare state and the principles on which its services should be distributed.

8. R. Boyson, 'Down with the poor' in E. Butterworth and R. Holman (eds), *Social Welfare in Modern Britain*, Fontana, 1975, pp. 381–7. Presents a liberal view of what is wrong with the welfare state and how its limitations can be overcome.

7
Does the family care?

INTRODUCTION

This chapter is concerned with an issue raised in Chapter 6 by sociologists concerned with the impact of social policy on women. It is concerned with the role of the family in health and welfare.

So far in this book, the debate about welfare provision has been rather narrowly presented, as the search for a balance between individual effort and state support. The impression that the debate is one of individual versus state provision is reinforced by the terms social scientists use in their analyses. We tend to equate health care with professional health care; we define social work as work exclusively performed by social workers. For example, GPs and health visitors are seen as providing the *primary* (rather than a back-up) health care team; GPs see 'patients', not fellow health workers, and health visitors see 'clients', not mothers caring for their families. In this emphasis on individuals as the consumers and not the producers of services, it is easy to lose sight of the informal help and support provided outside the welfare state. It is easy to forget that the welfare state presumes, and rests upon, this network of caring. The welfare state is not a comprehensive alternative to self-help; it is an institution which on certain conditions and in certain situations is prepared to shoulder some of the burden of care borne by families.

The image of a welfare state providing total support for individual clients and patients is thus an over-simple one. Instead, a major theme running through the history of social policy has been with maintaining a clear and extensive area of *family* responsibility. The debate has been one of state care versus family care. In this debate, individuals feature not in their consumer-role (as patients, clients and so on) but in their family role, as mothers, fathers, daughters, neighbours. Policy-makers have been concerned not so much with maintaining 'individual responsibility' in some general sense but with ensuring that parents fulfil their responsibilities to their young children and children meet their responsibilities to their elderly parents.

Translated into policy objectives, governments have sought to design policies which do not undermine a father's motivation to provide financial support for his family (see Chapter 4 on the Poor Law). Governments have been concerned, too, that their policies do not inadvertently encourage women to abandon their

106

traditional responsibilities to care for their partners and their children. It was on this criterion that policies aimed at reducing infant mortality and improving the health of working-class children were judged in the early twentieth century. And, on this criterion, the growth of maternity care was generally welcomed because it strengthened both mothers and the institution of motherhood. However, the 1906 Act which introduced school meals to improve child health was fiercely criticised by those who believed it would weaken the spirit of parental responsibility. 'To feed a child is to give relief to its parents, and the effect must be to undermine their independence and self-reliance and to give their children an object-lesson in the evasion of responsibility' (Sir Arthur Clay, 1906, 'The feeding of school children' in Evans, *Social Policy, 1830–1914*, 1978, p. 244).

Eighty years later, similar anxieties are still expressed. The provision of public services is seen to breed an overdependence on 'the nanny state'; to encourage a philosophy 'that parents may do what they like and it is the duty of the state to look after the children' (Patrick Jenkin, MP, in a speech to the National Children's Bureau Conference, 1979).

Chapter 7 explores some of these concerns about the modern family and the role of the welfare state in maintaining traditional family responsibilities. However, our attempt to discover more about the relationship between 'the family' and 'the welfare state' is hampered by two problems. First is the fact that Britain has never had something explicitly called a 'family policy'. Government thinking about the family therefore has to be gleaned in indirect ways, from a close examination of the legislation and the operation of welfare services. Secondly, not only is there no explicit policy about the family, but 'the family' as a single institution does not exist. Instead, there are many kinds of family. When talking about the elderly and handicapped, we generally think of the family as a kinship network spanning three generations, and involving relatives who do not necessarily live in the same households. When children are the focus of policy, the concept of the family takes on a more precise meaning. The family is typically regarded as a two-generation unit, consisting of a wage-earning father, a non-working mother and their children. But even here, variety is the norm. In 1981, one in ten families with children had an unemployed father and nearly half contained working mothers. In addition, one in eight families were one-parent families and in most of these it is the mother who takes responsibility both for financial provision and for childcare.

THE FAMILY: STRIPPED OF ITS FUNCTIONS?

One strand in the debate about the family looks at the changes which have occurred over the last 200 years and concludes that the family no longer cares for its kith and kin in the way that it did in former times. With the industrial revolution, the family lost its role as a unit producing goods for sale, to be left only with its role of consuming goods and producing people. The development of the welfare services, like education and health care, is seen to have resulted in the family reneging even on its minimal function of care and socialisation. The family has become simply a place where goods and services are consumed. The passage below outlines this argument.

Reading 1

Social scientists over the first half of this century took the position that . . . the family had been pressured into surrendering most of [its] functions to other social institutions. Despite the fact that research over the past twenty years has seriously questioned this conclusion, a significant number of those who are responsible for shaping social policies, administering programmes and delivering services, tend to operate on this earlier assumption. Since their actions have considerable impact on familes, it is useful to sketch the argument and the factors associated with the position. It was charged that initially the family lost its economic function to the industrial sector, leaving it with the residual functions of reproduction and the care of the socially dependent – children, the old and the sick. Industrial society created a family structure more suited to its needs than earlier forms which were likely to be characterized as more complete economic and political units composed of a number of sub-families, whose needs were met through an interdependent extended kin system.

While this concept of the extended family must be viewed as an ideal type rather than an empirical description of all pre-industrial families it does provide a number of insights. The extended family was large, it was both a production and consumption unit, and to some extent was relatively self-sufficient. Better suited to a farming society, it became unnecessary and counterproductive to a highly mechanised labour market. The extended family, unable to adjust to these new pressures, gradually disintegrated and a new structure, the nuclear family, gradually evolved. This new unit, composed of husband, wife and children, independent from their kin-related families, was viewed as the ideal structure for meeting the demands of geographical and occupational mobility . . .

The nuclear family evolved precisely because it met the criteria of efficiency and effectiveness required by the economic system.

As with any major shifts or changes there were bound to be casualties and in the absence of the extended care network, society accepted the responsibility of developing an infrastructure of formal social organizations to provide care for those unable to adjust. Those functions, previously carried out by families, were still viewed as important, but other institutions were judged to be more capable of undertaking them.

Earlier it was pointed out that the family was viewed as retaining certain residual functions: procreation, some elements of socialization, and the care of the dependent. In fact, these functions were not 'family' functions but were, more often than not, the responsibility of the women in the family. In time, these too were affected as larger numbers of mothers entered the labour force. The socialization of children was seen as a function that legitimately should be shared with other institutions. Examples of these are the introduction of compulsory education towards the end of the nineteenth century and the recent expansion of formal day-care programmes.

The process of birth and the care of the sick and infirm became the responsibility of the health system, leaving, it was argued, minimal socialization and recreational functions to the family. And now these developments, initiated over 150 years ago, have created a situation that many feel is serious. Families, either willingly or under external pressure, have given up many of the functions traditionally carried out by families and by seeking support for their members from other social institutions have become dependent on these institutions and the State. The idea of shared responsibility is no longer viable in present-day society since the family has little to share.

R. Moroney, *The Family and the State: Considerations for Social Policy*, 1976, pp. 16–17.

Questions
1. *How is the family of the past seen in this account of the modern family?*
2. *How did the nuclear family emerge?*
3. *What is meant by the 'minimal socialization and recreational functions' of the modern family?*

Over the last twenty years, further social changes are seen to have intensified an unhealthy dependency of the family on the state. The next reading is concerned with the role of the family in the care of the elderly, and identifies some of these changes.

Reading 2

The fact that recent official and public expressions of anxiety about dependency and the future of the community care have been solely concerned with the elderly is in large measure a reflection of their numerical importance in the population requiring care and of the projected growth in their numbers. It is, at the same time, a function of the rising cost of residential care for the elderly. Over the last twenty years, the numbers of people aged 65 and over have increased by one-third – some 2 million people. The most remarkable projected increase, however, is among those most likely to require care. There are currently about 3 million aged 75 and over and this total is likely to increase by 500,000 by 1990 . . . About 17 per cent of people over 75 currently require some regular form of care, either in residential institutions or in the community . . .

At the same time as the proportion of the elderly population requiring care is expanding, other demographic and social changes, including the decline in the birth-rate, delay in the age of parenthood, increase in divorce and in single-parent families and most importantly, the growth in the labour-market activity of women, has reduced the pool of potential caregivers. Economic activity rates among married women have nearly trebled over the last thirty years, until in 1979 some three-fifths were working. Although the recent growth in female employment has been predominantly in part-time work, the fact that working married women still perform two roles is bound to reduce their capacity to care for elderly relatives. Over the course of the 1970s the divorce rate increased four-fold and it has been estimated that one in four new marriages will end in divorce.* One-third of marriages are second marriages for at least one of the partners and this division of kin network will have implications for the provision of care. At the moment we can only speculate about the sources of care for the step-grandmothers and step-grand-fathers of the next century. More certain, however, is the fact that those elderly people who are currently divorced (2 per cent) receive fewer visits from relatives and are more isolated than other groups while those who are single are more likely than others to enter institutions.

These demographic and social changes raise important questions about the future of community care for the elderly and social planning for community care which go beyond the concerns of this chapter. But it is essential not to get these developments out of proportion. In the first place, while the growth of the elderly population is frequently discussed, paradoxically in detrimental terms, it actually represents a major national achievement in putting an end to many of the causes of premature death in childhood if not actually in later life. It is only the social response to increased longevity that should give rise to disappointment. Secondly, while there is a close association between advanced age and disability, the vast majority of elderly people are able to care for themselves entirely without help, or with only minimal support.

* latest estimates suggest one in three marriages will end in divorce.

A. Walker, 'Caring for elderly people: a conflict between women and the state' in J. Finch and D. Groves (eds), *A Labour of Love: Women, Work and Caring*, 1983, pp. 107–8.

Questions
1. *What social trends does Walker see as fuelling public concern about the care of the elderly?*
2. *In what ways is marital breakdown linked to the debate about community care?*

THE FAMILY: STILL CARING FOR ITS KITH AND KIN?

Research by historians over the last decade has questioned the image of the family depicted in the previous section. First, it questions our popular image of the famiy of the past as a stable, closely-knit unit providing high-quality care for its dependants. Secondly, it challenges our image of the modern family as unstable and geographically mobile, with a low commitment to the care of either its children or its elderly and handicapped members.

The reading below identifies a number of myths about the family of the past and the present.

Reading 3

As far as the myths are concerned, however hard we look, the stable community in which most of the population grew up and grew old together, living out their whole lives in one place, seems to have been very rare in most if not all of non-highland Britain at least since medieval times. As for the nineteenth century, work on a national sample from the 1851 Census of Great Britain suggests that well under half of the whole population was living in the place where they had been born, that around two fifths had moved from their place of birth by the time that they were 15 and that one child in every six had been geographically mobile by the time of his or her second birthday . . . Contrary to the popular view it was in the twentieth century that rent restriction, council housing and a fall in population growth rates produced in many areas more stable communities than had probably been found for hundreds of years . . .

[The available data do not support] another popular myth, the notion that people in the past regularly and unquestioningly took care of aged relatives. The modern practice of placing the aged in institutions is not new – in 1906 almost 6 per cent of the population aged 65 and over were living in Poor Law institutions; in 1966 1.9 per cent were living in homes for the aged, 1.7 per cent in hopsitals and 0.9 per cent in psychiatric institutions, an overall figure of 4.4 per cent. Right back into the early nineteenth century and beyond it is clear that the aged normally depended on poor relief for their support and that large numbers were in institutional care. Overall, the evidence would strongly suggest that the aged were only likely to live with, and be supported by, relatives where either they had property which gave them power over their relatives' future living standards or where their support was heavily subsidised by charity or by poor relief.

More generally, considerable doubt has in recent years been cast on the notion of the family of the past as a warm and altruistic institution. In some areas there seems evidence of a distinct calculative streak in relations between kin; one contemporary drew an analogy with attitudes to investment in a joint stock company. Some scholars have even gone so far as to argue that in Europe before the later eighteenth century little love and affection as we would know it existed in relations even between spouses and between parents and children. An extreme view, but it would be hard on the basis of present evidence to sustain an argument that people were on average more affectionate towards their children or that children had a higher priority in the everyday lives of families than they do today . . .

Another topic of considerable present day concern which equally looks less characteristically modern if seen from a long run historical perspective is marital dissolution and its effects on children . . . Comparing the earlier twentieth century marriage cohorts with the present reveals a marked increase in disruption through marital breakup of the lives of both adults and children (though once death is included the differences are perhaps less marked than some would have expected). But the earlier nineteenth century marriage cohorts show current patterns in a very different light. For pre-twentieth century marriages, at most marriage durations marital breakup rates closely paralleled modern ones (and given the death rates in the past, the proportion of children affected must have been considerably higher right through the nineteenth century and earlier). The problem of marital breakup is not, then, new; but we view it against a historical background where it was temporarily lower . . .

Finally, the myth of a new level of immorality in modern society is also one which needs handling with some care . . . Even at the high levels reached since 1960 the illegitimate birth rate was little if at all higher than in the mid-Victrian period. Few communities even today can match the ratio of 193 [illegitimate births per 1,000 births] recorded for three inland Banffshire parishes in 1861–65. And while we know that the percentage of couples engaging in premarital sex with their eventual husbands had reached 67 per cent even for the relatively staid group who married at ages 25–29 in the early 1970s, the modern figures have to be seen in a somewhat different long-run perspective when we note that around 60 per cent of women bearing their first child in the early nineteenth century seem to have conceived that child out of wedlock. Again, the more recent past – when premarital sex was clearly somewhat less frequent – should not be taken as a guide to what may have happened in an earlier society . . .

There is one further area which we have already touched on but which merits further discussion as another possible characteristic feature of the modern family: the changing nature of the family as an economic unit. While it is easy to romanticise the family of the past as one in which each contributed in work of one kind or another what he or she could, and all shared in the rewards which might or might not ensue, there is an important element of truth in this picture. Before the educational and

technical reforms of the later nineteenth century there were many
opportunities for children to contribute to the family economy
from an early age . . . The rise of factory textile work with its
employment opportunities for women and older children probably
conceals in fact a steady decline from the later eighteenth century
right up to the Second World War in the full time employment of
women outside the home and in the job opportunities available
to younger children.

> M. Anderson, 'What is new about the modern family: an historical
> perspective' in British Society for Population Studies, *The Family*,
> 1983, pp. 3–4 and 13.

Questions

1. *In what ways does the image of the family, past and present, differ
   from that presented in Reading 2?*
2. *What light does Anderson's account shed on the role of the state in the
   care of the elderly in the nineteenth and early twentieth century? What
   light does it shed on the current concern with the care of the elderly?*
3. *How have the rates of marital dissolution changed over the last 180
   years?*

Anderson's research points to an alternative interpretation of the
modern family, as a unit which cares for its families in ways that
families have previously found impossible. The recognition that
families *do* care has prompted social scientists to look more
closely at how they do it. This focus on family care has been
reinforced by changes in government policy towards preventive
health and community care. Prevention and community care have
been strongly promoted, particularly since the mid-1970s, as a
way of shifting both the responsibility and cost of caring from the
state to the family. The policies of prevention and community
care thus represent a way of altering the balance between the two
major caring institutions in Britain.

It is increasingly acknowledged that community care is
provided largely by women. With the development of such
policies, women can find themselves caught in a cycle of caring:
caring for children, then for elderly relatives and finally for aged
spouses. Caring full-time for dependants is only possible if
women themselves remain economically dependent: on their
husbands or on the state. The idea that dependency is socially
created was explored in Chapter 4. The fact that women's
dependency springs, at least in part, from their role in coping
with the dependency of others provides further support for this
perspective.

The reading below, taken from a recent survey of carers,

examines the meaning of community care for those caring for elderly and handicapped relatives.

Reading 4

No satisfactory term exists for the group of individuals whose problems are highlighted in this report – those caring for dependants on an unpaid basis. The absence of a satisfactory term is perhaps itself indicative of the lack of social awareness regarding this role. Despite its shortcomings, the term 'carer' has been used to describe these individuals . . .

The concept of community care is not new; the greater part of care for dependent groups has always taken place in the community in some form or other. Since the 1940s, however, when the principle of a comprehensive statutory-based care system really gained acceptance, the emphasis of state provision has shifted by degrees from institutional care to community-based care. Successive governments have shown interest in extending community care to groups once considered only suitable for institutionalisation, and various pieces of legislation have sought to encourage local authorities to provide services in keeping with the community care philosophy.

Moreover, this philosophy has itself changed over the years. Early thinking concentrated on providing care 'in' the community, placing importance on the role of relatively small-scale, local residential accommodation. In the late 1960s and early 1970s, the idea of care 'by' the community gained ground, and this period saw an expansion in the provision of day-care centres, domiciliary services, and aids and adaptations in an attempt to improve conditions for the disabled and their families. More recently the promotion of citizen participation and the use of volunteers has been the keynote, and politicians have placed considerable stress on the importance of 'informal caring networks' of support by family, friends and neighbours.

It is clear, however, that the growth in domiciliary services has not been sufficient to sustain the declared aims of the government's community care policies. It is equally clear that for many elderly or disabled people, extensive informal caring systems do not exist and that effectively they are cared for by their immediate family only. For the most part, then, community care can be regarded as family care . . .

That carers are predominantly women has been well demonstrated. In the 1950s, Townsend's study of *The Family Life of*

Old People showed that the family system of care was organised around female relatives, particularly daughters. Twenty years on, in 1978, an Equal Opportunities Commission survey found that three times as many women as men were looking after elderly or handicapped relatives. Similarly, the study conducted by Crossroads* in 1979 found that daughters, mothers, wives, sisters and daughters-in-law constituted the great majority of carers . . .

Hunt,[1] in her 1965 survey of women's employment, drew particular attention to the fact that working women who were married were more likely to have caring responsibilities than those who were single. This is an important point because the popular image of the carer tends to be that of the single female relative, rather than of the married woman, whose problems are often insufficiently recognised. It is also important because married women, and in certain circumstances divorced and widowed women, are excluded from receiving certain benefits which are available to others who care for dependants.

The financial attraction to government of a community (or family) care policy is clear for institutional care is expensive.

Local authorities are facing shrinking budgets and the associated 'rationing' of services. Given scarce resources, social services departments tend to put priority on providing for the old and severely handicapped living alone. This may well mean that, regardless of their ability to cope, the family – or the nearest female relative – are left with no alternative but to provide for their dependent relatives on their own. Several studies have underlined the important role that female relatives play in preventing the admission of the elderly handicapped to institutional care, leaving available resources for those individuals who live alone.

Whilst this policy may be economically expedient for local authorities; its implications can be severe for the families caring for dependants who, without adequate support, may find it very difficult to cope. In this light the government's 'community care' policy is revealed as a euphemism for an under-resourced system which places heavy burdens on *individual* members of the community, most of them women. It represents care 'on the cheap'.

* The Crossroads Care Attendants Scheme provides care-attendants to relieve the carers of severely disabled people at those times of the day which are most critical for the carer.

1. A. Hunt, *A Survey of Women's Employment*, HMSO, 1968.

Equal Opportunities Commission, *Caring for the Elderly and Handicapped: Community Care Policies and Women's Lives*, 1982, pp. viii and 1–3.

Questions

1. *In what ways has the meaning of community care changed over the last half century?*
2. *Why are women more likely to care for the disabled and handicapped than men? What effect do you think this division of responsibility has on women?*
3. *Why is community care identified as care 'on the cheap'?*

The reading above, like the one by Alan Walker earlier in the chapter, raises some of the issues involved in community care. The issues raised relate primarily to the costs of caring for the family and for the state. They look at the transaction of care through the eyes of the givers rather than the receivers. However, the debate about community care is centrally concerned with those on the receiving end of care.

The section below looks briefly at this wider debate. It focuses on the position of children in the care of local authorities.

CHILDREN IN CARE: AT HOME OR AWAY?

Children in care are those for whom the local authority has assumed parental rights and responsibilities. Taking a child into care invariably involves judgements about the capacity of his or her natural parents to make adequate provision for the family. This view of family incompetence has long been part of Britain's childcare legislation. Under the 1834 Poor Law, destitute parents were separated from their children in segregated workhouses where they could neither have more children nor influence the development of the ones they already had. In 1889, the Poor Law (Children's Act) empowered the Poor Law Guardians to assume parental rights over any child in their care, once they were satisfied that the natural parents were irresponsible. Today's legislation carefully stipulates the conditions on which local authorities can assume parental rights. Childcare proceedings can be initiated where a child is abandoned or at risk of physical abuse or, more vaguely, 'when the habits and mode of life make a parent unfit to have care of his child' (Child Care Act, 1980, Section 3).

While modern legislation embodies some of the nineteenth-century principles, it has moved beyond them in its attempt to recognise the legal rights of the child. In the process, it has considerably reduced the rights of natural parents, and, some argue, shifted the balance of rights towards the state. By law, local authorities must seek to place their children in environments which best meet their needs and best protect their interests. This environment could be a residential home, a foster home or the home of the child's natural parents.

Over the last thirty years, the pendulum has swung against residential homes as the best environment for children in long-term care. Children's homes are seen to 'institutionalise' children (see Goffman in Chapter 3). They are seen, too, to prevent the development of a close parent–child bond which the research of John Bowlby indicated was essential to normal mental and emotional health. Finally, institutions are seen to stigmatise their inmates (see Chapter 4). With these changing attitudes to residential care, came an increasing emphasis on the value of family life, particularly within the expanding profession of social work. A second option developed in the 1950s and 1960s; care by the child's natural family with appropriate support and counselling from professionals. Over the last two decades, this option, too, has waned in popularity. It is fostering which is seen to provide the kind of family care children need but which their own parents are unable to provide.

Deciding on a child's future 'in its best interests' raises complex and often intractable problems. It is clearly not possible to capture this complexity in a few selected readings. The passages below can therefore do no more than point to some of the issues involved. Because many of the arguments against residential care have been rehearsed in earlier chapters of the book, readings have been selected which challenge the view that foster care is necessarily the best alternative.

The fifth reading looks at the model of the family associated with foster care. It looks, too, at the resource-implications of a shift in policy towards fostering, noting in particular what this shift means for 'natural' parents facing difficulties in maintaining their families.

Reading 5

Family care does not always mean care in the family of origin or in the natural family – foster homes are replacing institutions and professional foster homes are beginning to undertake the assessment and care of delinquents. Similarly the fostering of mentally handicapped adults and the elderly mentally infirm confirms the caring, nursing view of the family. The state brings about subtle changes in this new emphasis. Whereas institutional care used to mean that a patient or child could be expected to rest and recuperate then return to his own home, foster care may represent more permanent change. Not only does it call for response and loyalty from the child and make visits from natural parents more difficult, but it does not automatically lead to a return home.

It is as though the relationship aspects of family life now take second place to the caring/nursing aspects and the family is valued for its caring capacity, rather than being seen as a grouping of individuals linked by a network of relationships which locate and provide status for individuals in a complex society. Such relationships cannot easily be set aside and the recipients of care are aware of the conflict of loyalties and are not always clear that they prefer foster family life to that of an institution . . .

The development of substitute care in foster homes and adoption homes has expanded recently following the 1975 Children's Act. It takes place at the expense of Day Care Services, and also at the expense of expanded advice services and cash grants to natural families. The implicit statement in all this is either that it is not cost effective to support struggling families, or that substitute families quite frequently provide a better environment for children than natural families. Thus, various changes of emphasis in recent Acts have driven social workers to look energetically for new homes rather than spend a great deal of energy enabling natural families to live together. The welfare of the child principle, which is intended to safeguard the rights of the child, may well diminish the weight which used to be put upon mothers' request to keep their children. In effect this principle frequently means that policy which the social worker believes will best meet the child's needs.

The social worker carries a heavy responsibility for interpretation because the child himself is rarely permitted to attend his own reviews and parents are frequently not invited to attend despite DHSS support for the idea. Even where parents are invited to attend reviews, it is likely that the foster parent rather than the natural parent will come, and it is by no means self-evident who speaks with most authority for the child's best interests.

The welfare principle requires that, so far as practicable, the wishes and feelings of the child should be ascertained when a decision is made . . . [However], it is possible that the welfare principle extends the rights of local authorities more than the rights of children and in a broad sense this seems to mean a diminution of family or parental rights . . .

In order to support family life and enable families to care for

their own, a policy of family services needs to be implemented
. . . It is clear that society shows its belief in family life by the
implementation of family-oriented policies – by avoiding unemployment, by providing adequate housing and by paying
adequate attention to mothers' health problems.

If society fails to establish those services which provide general
support to families (by reducing levels of poverty, stress,
insecurity, ill-health and bad housing), then families will be seen
to be providing inadequate care and social workers will have to
become involved in rescuing children and placing them elsewhere.
If services do not improve it will be increasingly difficult for such
families to hold their own, or retain care of their children: many
will fail. This, in the past, has been labelled unsympathetically as
'caring neglect' and prior to 1948 the tendency was to place the
child in an institution. Today substitute family care is fast
replacing institutional care, and families who cannot have
children of their own hold their homes open to children in need.
How much does it matter that we have failed to prevent those
children from needing a substitute family?

V. Macleod, *Whose Child?*, 1983, pp. 56–8.

Questions
1. *What does Macleod mean when she says 'the relationship aspects of
   family life now take second place to the caring/nursing aspects'?*
2. *According to Macleod, how has the development of fostering affected
   the family services provided by local authorities, the work of social
   workers and the position of families struggling to survive?*
3. *What problems does Macleod identify in the principle of 'in the best
   interests of the child'?*
4. *What kind of policy does the author suggest would better support the
   family?*

The final reading in this chapter provides one child's account of
her experiences in a foster home and a children's home.

Reading 6

I was thirteen when I was taken into care. Some arrangements
had already been made and I knew what was going to happen to
me . . .

My foster parents had two sons of their own, one aged twenty-one and one a year younger than me and a year below me at school. They also had another foster daughter, she was eighteen and had been living with them since she was fourteen. It was with these last two that I had the most contact and it was they who mostly influenced my feelings whilst I was actually with the foster parents. Towards the young son I was jealous, I think I was rather sensitive while I was there – I think it was mostly because I didn't feel very secure there. I couldn't really understand why they wanted me and I didn't really see any reason why they should put up with me . . .

The most striking feature of the boarding out was the loneliness, I was one child, a stranger with a family. The family had been going on for years and could not really be expected to adapt itself to me, and yet I was not old enough to adapt myself to people – not really. It was rather like a tug-of-war – and in turns they expected that, 'I am doing so much for you, surely I deserve something in return', and that something in return always seemed to be far more than I could give. My loyalty – it couldn't be turned swiftly like that in a couple of months from one family I had just left to another family that I was just getting to know and yet it was expected of me, and I had to be on my best behaviour – there was no room for moods and tantrums. I was a visitor in the house all the time . . . It is so obvious to the foster child that they are the ones that don't fit in and they are the ones that feel that they have got to do the hard work and to change themselves to fit in with the family and the family are such a tight circle, you have to work so hard to get into it. It is rather like an exclusive club . . .

I can't think why there is so much controversy about foster parents versus Children's Homes, Institutions versus foster parents – there is no comparison. In a Children's Home there is nothing except good behaviour demanded of a child – no loyalty and they don't have to fight their way into the circle – it is accepted in its own terms. No one has more right than another, there is no feeling that you have to be loyal to the houseparent and forsake your own. It is a neutral sort of place where you can go and recover from whatever has happened to you or get ready for the next step – Gosh! – there is no comparison at all between Homes and foster parents. I was infinitely happier in the Reception Centre and in the Family Group Home and given a choice, I would never have gone to foster parents, a Children's

Home was there specially for the children and there was no doubt about whether you are wanted or not or whether you fit in or not – it doesn't matter – it's just a choice place on earth because you know that they have got to look after you and all you have to do is behave yourself and that is not difficult. Of course, there is no doubt that if it could be guaranteed to work, there is no doubt that the child would fit in and a magic word could be said – nothing would be better than the family situation. In a Children's Home there is always the feeling that I have not got a proper mummy and daddy, I have not got an ordinary home to go back to. I live in a Children's Home and that makes me a little bit different, but advantages far outweigh the disadvantages and you are free from the eternal questioning and 'Am I wanted?' 'Am I being good?'

> 'A children's home/a foster home compared' in N. Timms, *The Receiving End*, 1973, pp. 44–8.

Questions

1. *Why does the author prefer an institution to a foster home?*
2. *What are the implications of what she is saying for the developments outlined in Reading 5?*
3. *Does her account undermine the arguments developed by Goffman and Townsend (see Chapter 4) against institutional care for other dependent groups like the elderly and the mentally ill?*

ESSAY QUESTIONS

1. 'In small-scale societies the welfare of the individual is assured through the bonds of kinship and neighbourhood. This is what we have lost in modern societies.' Evaluate this statement with reference to Britain. (adapted from JMB, 1979)

2. What is meant by 'community care'? Critically evaluate the evidence on the principle and practice of community care with reference to elderly and disabled people.

3. What light have research studies thrown upon the suitability of residential care? Critically evaluate the relevant evidence and the policies influenced by it, by reference to the residential care of *either* children *or* old people. (JMB, 1979)

4. 'Society shows its belief in family life by the implementation of family-oriented policies – by avoiding unemployment, by providing adequate housing and by paying adequate attention to mothers' health problems' (Macleod, *Whose Child?*). Critically examine this statement in the light of the growth of foster care for children taken into the care of local authorities.

FURTHER READING

1. E. Craven, L. Rimmer and M. Wicks, *Family Issues and Public Policy*, Study Commission on the Family, 1982.

   Examines recent changes in family life in Britain, and a range of social policies which may promote family welfare in the future.

2. M. Nissel, *The Welfare State: Diversity and Decentralisation*, Policy Studies Institute, 1980, pp. 4–21.

   Examines whether and in what ways the responsibilities carried by families have changed in the period since the Second World War and describes the current range of services provided by the state for families in the field of housing, education, health care and personal social services.

3. C. Rossiter and M. Wicks, *Crisis or Challenge? Family Care, Elderly People and Social Policy*, Study Commission on the Family, 1982.

   Looks at recent changes in the position of the elderly and in the provision of services by the state and the family.

4. New Society Social Studies Reader, *Social Work*, New Society, 1981. Articles by M. Colley on 'David: the boy who didn't want care', C. Melotte, 'Why children are taken into care' and T. Hopkins, 'Child care at a profit'.

   Looks at some of the difficult issues involved in the decision to take a child into care.

5. J. Oliver, 'The caring wife' in J. Finch and D. Groves, *Caring: A Labour of Love*, Routledge and Kegan Paul, 1983.

   Describes the feelings and experiences of married women caring for disabled husbands and the kinds of services which improve the quality of their lives.

6. H. Land and R. Parker, 'United Kingdom' in S. Kamerman and A. Kahn (eds), *Family Policy*, Columbia University Press, 1978, pp. 331–66.

   Surveys the assumptions made about families and family responsibility in British social policy by focusing on the principle and practice of three areas of welfare: social security and taxation, housing and the provision of care for dependants.

8

The future of the welfare state

INTRODUCTION

Controversy is very much a feature of current social policies in the field of health and welfare. Yet this book has suggested that controversy is not new. Instead, opposition, vociferous and effective, has long accompanied announcements by governments of their intention to build up or pare down welfare services. The climate of consensus which lasted from the Second World War to the mid-1970s has perhaps dulled people's awareness of the fact that the idea of a welfare state has been debated for over 200 years.

The idea of a welfare state sparks controversy because it touches on a number of basic questions about society as it is and could become. These questions were outlined in the Introduction to the book and have been raised, in various ways, in all the chapters. How social scientists view the future of the welfare state is closely tied to their attitude to freedom, equality and democracy, their assessment of capitalism and their explanations of suffering.

Recent social changes have given these reflections a new political urgency. Demographic changes lengthen waiting lists for medical care at the same time as the discovery of new and more expensive forms of treatment (like open heart surgery and renal dialysis) increase the costs of care. The same demographic changes increase the costs of social security, as the number of pensioners rise and their period of retirement lengthens. In addition to the long-term demographic changes, there is the more recent increase in dependency brought about by fundamental changes in the economy. There has been a sharp deterioration in Britain's economic performance since the mid-1970s, a deterioration measured in a low growth rate and a sustained increase in unemployment over the last decade. Reinforcing the upward trend in unemployment has been a government determined to reduce 'over manning' in the private and public sectors, which, together with the wider process of technological change, is transforming patterns of employment particularly among the working class. The effect of these different forces is that the traditional areas of employment for skilled and semi-skilled

124

workers (manufacturing, ship-building, retail and clerical work) are shedding labour, while the new high-technology industries achieve their high productivity with only a small labour force.

All these factors are combining to increase dependency, inequality and poverty in Britain. Rates of unemployment among eighteen- and nineteen-year-olds increased by 180 per cent between 1979 and 1984, with over one quarter unemployed in 1984. In 1983, seven million people were dependent on supplementary benefit, the system that was set up after the Second World War as a short-term measure to provide a minimum income for those not covered by Beveridge's national insurance scheme. While seven million people depended on the state for their poverty-line income, another eight million lived in or close to poverty. A large proportion of these were low-paid workers. Taken together, fifteen million people (one in four of the population) were living in, or on the margins of, poverty in 1983.

With the increase in dependency, the burden of tax has risen, particularly for low-paid workers. In 1960, a typical family living on two-thirds average earnings (around the poverty line) would have paid no income tax. In 1983, the same family paid 20 per cent of its income in tax and national insurance.

These facts are widely recognised. In discussing their implications for future social policy, social scientists tend to take one of two positions. Some argue that in response to the problems of increasing dependency, the welfare state should be increased in scope and changed in style. Those working within a conflict or a social democratic perspective tend to favour greater economic planning and more social intervention. Social scientists who identify with the market liberals argue for a very different response to the issue of dependency. They favour a greatly reduced welfare state, involving the minimum of economic management and the minimum of state provision. This position is associated with the New Right within the Conservative Party. The 'New Right', however, is something of a misnomer: as we noted in Chapter 6, their ideas are very old, dating back over 200 years.

In identifying only two sides to a complex debate, the chapter is simplifying the arguments about the welfare state. As Chapter 6 indicates, there are profound differences within the Marxist, feminist and social democratic perspectives here identified as broadly in favour of a welfare state. There are also differences, of policy but not of principle, among the liberal school. This chapter can only indicate some of the areas of controversy and some of the policy options favoured and opposed by those concerned with health and welfare in the future.

REBUILDING THE WELFARE STATE
Social scientists who subscribe to conflict and social democratic

perspectives on the welfare state are broadly in favour of maintaining it, albeit in a radically different form. Their argument is based on the answers they provide to the four basic questions identified in the Introduction to the book. They emphasise equality, democracy and a particular kind of freedom, freedom from dependency, as the goals of a civilised society. They see capitalist society as a society which creates both inequality and dependency, and which offers little prospect of escape to those trapped at the bottom of the ladder. They see poverty and ill-health as the result of the injustices of the market system and not as a sign of individual inadequacy.

Reflecting these views, social scientists within the conflict and social democratic models argue for stronger and more far-reaching social policies. They propose that the sphere of social policy is widened to include areas traditionally seen to belong to the economy on the one hand and the family on the other. Social policy would thus include policies on employment and on the care of children and elderly in the home.

Widening the scope of social policy is seen as necessary to tackle inequality and dependency at its source, in the distribution of work and wealth in the labour market and in the family. A wide range of policies are proposed to alter this distribution of work and wealth.

First, emphasis is given to the need for a greater equality of incomes between rich and poor, wage-earners and claimants, men and women, white and black. To this end, social scientists argue for policies which break down the traditional divisions within the labour market and the social security system. For example, they argue for full employment, with a minimum and maximum wage; they argue for greater equality between wages and benefits, challenging our traditional ideas that those who 'earn' a living should receive more than those who 'scrounge' from the state. They argue, too, for a breakdown of divisions within social security and, in particular, the division between means-tested and insurance benefits. They argue for an abolition of the contribution principle and the means test, raising benefits for all categories of dependants to a level which enables those who are unable to work to share in society's wealth.

Secondly, expansion of welfare services is emphasised. Social scientists preserve Beveridge's idea of 'a social wage'; the provision of services in kind, like education and health care, which otherwise would be paid for from individual wage packets. The social wage is seen as particularly important for those on state benefits, maintaining their access to a reasonable standard of education, housing, health care and transport when money incomes are low. While arguing for the further development of collectively-provided services, social scientists propose a different model of state provision. They emphasise the need for community control of services, a control which will help reduce the present power imbalance between the providers and receivers of welfare.

The first reading is concerned with the question of money, with reducing poverty and inequality by promoting full employment and a guaranteed living 'wage' for all, regardless of their employment status. It argues that, at present, Britain adheres to an 'earnings ethic' in which those who earn their living are seen as superior to those who don't.

Reading 1

Our mistake over the last decade and a half – if not since the war – has been to forget the social policy primacy of full employment and to let it become a matter for economists to discuss in largely technical terms. The objective of this chapter is to reinforce the arguments for putting full employment back among the main objectives of social planning despite the difficulty of achieving it . . .

Full employment is one vital precondition for the satisfactory achievement of other objectives, not just the reduction of poverty and inequality. Past policies to integrate groups into society and remove the barriers of disadvantage and privilege are predicated upon sustained low unemployment. If it cannot be achieved, then we need to redesign quite radically many of the programmes and strategies associated with what is popularly called the 'welfare state'.

A particularly clear example is the current foot-dragging, if not outright obstruction, by the Manpower Services Commission and other government agencies at central, regional and local level, over helping disabled people into work and assisting them once they are employed. There can be no clearer illustration of Richard Titmuss' remark that those who are regarded as 'essential manpower' during periods of labour shortage are treated as 'surplus labour' during recession. The main measures to help disabled people in the labour force derive from the Disabled Persons (Employment) Acts introduced during wartime labour scarcity, and there has been a signal failure to adapt these to the very changed labour market conditions of recent years in ways that enhance the position of disabled people . . .

Greater sexual and racial equality are also jeopardised by the recession. Even the limited gains in employment made by women in the early and mid-1970s already seem to have been eroded by rising unemployment. These groups tend to lose out doubly amid high unemployment. They are less able to obtain jobs and also receive less public support for special measures when those long established in the labour force are in fear of their own jobs. This atmosphere is a fertile one for scapegoating those seen as 'outsiders'. Married women have experience of this but racial, ethnic and religious groups suffer the most. This is 'the misery that generates hate', as Beveridge put it at the start of his *Full Employment in a Free Society* . . .

[For those outside the labour market] the link between unemployment, especially prolonged unemployment, and poverty must be broken. The evidence on the persistence of this link has been clear for many years . . .Now it is not only very much more thoroughly documented but very much larger numbers of people are actually experiencing the rigours of prolonged unemployment. Successive cuts in state benefits have made the hardships worse . . .

. . . Linked to adequate benefits, we need to devise ways of countering the stigma that attaches to being out of work and demoralises the unemployed and their families. Early retirement of course might allow some to achieve what is currently seen as a more honourable status, but selective help of this type runs the danger of reinforcing the lower standing of the majority who remain unemployed. At present the government with its clear insistence on Unemployment Review Officers as a major weapon in its 'crackdown on scroungers' reinforces the stigma . . . We must . . . acknowledge that the state reflects as well as shapes wider public views and prejudices against those who are seen as failing to work. At the very least, [the continuing high level of unemployment] requires that opportunities to participate in and contribute to society in ways that are properly valued and respected are available to all members of society, whether employed or not. At present many contributions are little valued and consequently appallingly rewarded, however essential they may be. But the process is circular; in our society too little is valued or respected that is not financially rewarded.

This perhaps is the central dilemma of what is called 'the work ethic', a term that has received surprisingly little analysis in recent years despite its frequent use. I would prefer to describe it as 'the *earnings* ethic'. We 'work' for our living, we have 'earned' our place. Historically the labour movement has had considerable difficulty with the problem of how we support those who are not working. Those who have worked *earn* their retirement benefit, but what about those who have never been able to work?

. . . The traditional labour movement view is that injury or disability acquired at work *earns* some greater acknowledgement, and so compensation, than other disabilities, even those such as the thalidomide injuries which children have brought into the world with them. We have to devise strategies to break the 'earnings ethic' and make full citizenship possible for those who do not work. Policies to move back towards high employment need to provide resources to give workers more real freedom to choose for how many hours and how many years they wish to work; by providing them with better and more secure career structures with opportunities to train; by enabling them to change careers and obtain suitable help to retrain; and by allowing them to work and serve the community in ways other than those currently classified as employment without subjecting them to deprivation and stigma.

> A. Sinfield, 'The necessity for full employment' in H. Glennerster, *The Future of the Welfare State*, 1983, pp. 61–3, 71–2.

Questions
1. *Explain why Sinfield attaches such importance to full employment.*
2. *In what ways does Sinfield see the recession jeopardising greater sexual and racial equality?*
3. *How does he suggest tackling the poverty and stigma experienced by those without paid employment?*
4. *What does the author mean by 'the earnings ethic'? Do you think that the ethic is a dominant one in Britain?*

The second reading is concerned with the promotion of sex equality. The promotion of equality between the sexes, it argues, is inextricably linked to the creation of a society which values and rewards informal caring as much as paid work. Again, social change is seen to depend on a coordinated programme of social and economic policies.

Reading 2
The state has never taken anything but a tiny share of the responsibility for the work of caring – for children, for men, for the sick and the old; women still do most of it and most of it unpaid. Indeed as a result of the public expenditure cuts since the mid-1970s, many public services which did do a little of the work of caring have been reduced or even withdrawn . . .

In future, if reducing inequalities between men and women is to be taken seriously as an objective, social policies have to be framed, administered and delivered using a different set of assumptions about the division of responsibilities for caring both within the family and between the family and the wider socio-economic system. In other words, reducing inequalities between men and women is not only a problem for women but also a problem for men . . .

Specifically, we would argue that, realistically, equal opportunities between men and women can only be achieved if it is recognised that men, too, may have responsibilities for caring and that they are entitled to exercise these. In this respect, the whole notion of the 'family wage' must be scrutinised and it must be made clear that the family has never been fully maintained simply through the male wage.

The wage system cannot provide for the differing needs of families as they move through the family life cycle. A shorter working week, of say twenty-five hours, would make this even more obvious. Adequate child benefits are clearly necessary and as a first step they could be doubled immediately for all children if the married man's tax allowance were abolished. In the longer term there are fundamental questions to be asked about what wages are for and how family income should be adjusted to family size. A shorter working day (rather than a shorter working week) must be one of the most immediate demands necessary to achieve this goal of equality in caring . . . Allied to this is the need to recognise that such caring may periodically affect availability for paid employment. We would wish to see not only a shorter working day, but entitlement, through the national insurance system, as is already possible in other Western European countries such as France, to time off with cash benefits to care for sick relatives, be they dependent children, spouses, disabled or elderly relatives. This leave should be irrespective of the sex of the carer . . .

We would also like to see services and facilities financed by the state to enable those with caring responsibilities to exercise them adequately. We would not, however, wish to see the services and facilities of the health and personal social services necessarily managed by the state, as a central bureaucracy. Rather we would like them to be locally based, in neighbourhoods sufficiently close to home to ease the burden of care. They should be community controlled and managed by democratically elected, neighbourhood councils, which would include those most intimately involved in caring for children, the sick and the old . . . If women who have had experience of such care had more opportunities for being involved in the formulation of policies as well as the administration of such services we would develop very different kinds of systems.

In sum, we are arguing that, if our goal is equal opportunities between men and women, our views and assumptions about not only social policies but also economic policies and family relationships must be radically changed. We might eventually reach a situation in which sex was not the main criterion by which we allocated care and maintenance in our society. Men and women would have equal claims on the labour market, the state and the family, while care would be work of central value in our society.

> M. David and H. Land, 'Sex and social policy' in H. Glennerster,
> *The Future of the Welfare State*, pp. 138–9, 152–4.

Questions

1. *Explain why the authors argue that the assumptions about who-does-what in the home will need to be re-thought if women are to achieve greater equality with men in employment and the family.*
2. *What is meant by the family wage?*
3. *Why do you think David and Land state 'the wage system cannot provide for the differing needs of families as they move through the family life cycle'?*
4. *How might locally-based and community-controlled services help with the problems of stigma and the invisible costs of seeking medical care identified in Chapters 4 and 5?*

DISMANTLING THE WELFARE STATE

Market liberals have consistently argued for a reduction in collective provision and an expansion of private provision. Their argument is based on the clear and unequivocal answers they provide to the questions outlined in the Introduction of the book. As Chapter 6 indicated, they emphasise personal freedom (to sell and spend) as the central feature of British society, more valued than equality and democracy. They see the capitalist economy as a freedom-promoting economy, one in which hard work is rewarded with wealth. They thus see poverty as a manifestation of individual differences rather than of structured inequalities. Moreover, a free market is seen to need such inequality to function efficiently; poverty acts as a spur to success.

Given these views, it is not surprising to find market liberals universally hostile to the policies presented in the earlier section. They are seen simply to repeat the old mistakes, but on a larger scale.

First, they reject the idea of government intervention in the economy. They reject the policies of positive discrimination favoured by Sinfield and reject, too, any weakening of the divisions between earners and claimants. They argue that the social security system has already reduced the incentive to work among the poor, thus increasing the number of claimants supported by the taxpayers.

Reading 3

In the world of commercial insurance it is understood that if a person is completely covered against all risk of loss – whether from fire and burglary, or even from accidents and illness – he is likely to behave less carefully in minimising costs. Thus comprehensive cover against the cost of car repairs and medical care will incline at least some motorists to take more risks. It is to minimise such perverse effects that car and health insurance policies require claimants to pay a proportion of the cost, just as theft insurance may require the householder to fit effective locks and other safety devices.

Students of insurance use the term 'moral hazard' to describe this danger that policy-holders will take less care to reduce any costs against which they can insure . . .

A precisely similar dilemma confronts all public or private philanthropy aimed at protecting people from poverty. Wherever relief is conditional on evidence of 'need', it inevitably weakens the general impulse of self-help for all but the most independently minded who still feel a stigma about 'charity', or the most severely handicapped who cannot anyway help themselves. Thus if a means test takes account of an individual's capital, it must tend to discourage thrift or encourage the dissipation of savings.

It is an economic merit of private charity that the donor can discriminate arbitrarily in favour of the 'deserving' poor and impose limits or conditions to contain costs. It is the political disadvantage of public 'compassion' (at taxpayers' expense) that it more often operates progressively to raise benefits, extend their coverage and remove or weaken such conditions as the now largely defunct test for unemployment benefit of [those] 'genuinely seeking work'. Even Keynes before the war acknowledged that the availability of a 'dole' that was modest by today's standards contributed to 'voluntary unemployment', especially for people who would have been able to earn only a low income by taking a job . . . The spread of such costly, ill-devised welfare policies throughout Europe and North America must help explain the difficulties so many governments now have in extricating their economies from the unholy combination of high inflation and rising unemployment . . .

Yet until the economic cost of moral hazard is tackled by cutting direct taxes and containing the cost of social benefits the prospect for rapidly declining unemployment must remain remote.

> R. Harris, 'Economic effects of moral hazard' in H. Parker, *The Moral Hazard of Social Benefits*, 1982, pp. 19–21.

Questions

1. *What is meant by 'moral hazard'? What relevance does the concept have for our understanding of social security and its system of means-tested and universal benefits?*

2. *Why does the author maintain that private charity is better able to avoid moral hazard than publicly-financed welfare services?*

3. *What proposals does Harris make to cut the cost of welfare benefits? In what ways would these proposals change the position of claimants?*

4. *Compare Harris's arguments and proposals with those developed by Sinfield in Reading 1.*

Market liberals reject the second main strategy advanced by those who support the idea of a welfare state; the expansion of the social wage. Instead, they advocate a radical reduction in state services. Cutting the collective provision of health and welfare services would achieve two objectives. It would result in greater personal freedom, through lower taxes, and in greater personal responsibility, through private insurance. Tax is seen as a major infringement of personal freedom. 'An essential part of economic freedom is freedom to choose how to use our income: how much to spend on ourselves and on what items, how much to save; how much to give away and to whom. Currently, more than 40% of our income is disposed of on our behalf by government' (Friedman and Friedman, *Free to Choose*, 1980, p. 65).

Reducing the burden of tax requires a major reduction in publicly-funded services. Reducing welfare spending, in turn, increases the incentives for individuals to take responsibility for themselves. The main proposal here is for a shift from collectively-funded systems of health care and social security to a system of personal insurance to cover the costs of illness, unemployment and old age. Individuals pay the fees for their own welfare services directly through insurance premiums, rather than indirectly through their taxes. To enable the poor to meet the cost of their health care and pensions, some redistribution of income is advocated. It would, however, have to be sufficiently limited to keep the tax burden on the majority well below its current level. Necessarily, those with higher incomes would enjoy better housing, education, health care and pensions, but these higher incomes are seen only to reflect their superior work performance. For those unable to meet the cost of personal insurance, the state would provide a safety-net of services, distributed on the basis of a means test.

These elements of the new welfare programme are outlined in the reading below.

Reading 4

In retrospect we can now see what should have been done in the past 50 years to anticipate the argument for a welfare state to supply massive services in kind. For this is where the most damage has been done. It is the services in kind – education and medical care – that are the fount of its objectionable elements of political influence, bureaucracy, paternalism, and not least its destruction of choice in markets, which other English-speaking countries have preserved, in addition to treating their poor better than we do.

First, the state should much sooner on a larger scale have re-distributed income in the form of purchasing power – generalised in cash or earmarked by voucher. The case for redistribution by social benefits in kind would not have gathered force and the con-flict between welfare and freedom could have been largely avoided.

Second, all social benefits should have been related closely to individual circumstances, not least the capacity to earn and the amount of earnings. But instead of the sensitive, humane refinement of means tests as measures of entitlement to social benefits, the welfare state has developed benefits distributed universally irrespective of circumstances, requirements or prefer-ences – all in the name of equality. The massive superiority of selective benefits is an intellectual battle that has now been won, but the victory came too late to prevent the creation of monstrous universal benefits that will require grievous effort to repeal.

Third, insofar as the state, for administrative convenience or economies in large-scale supply, provided services in kind, it should have financed them not by taxation from non-users as well as from users, but by charges from all users according to the extent of their use, with low incomes 'topped up' to enable the relatively poor to pay . . .

The first obstacle [to such policies being implemented] is the whole body of thought that has looked to the state to cure almost every ill – from unemployment and inflation to poverty and inequality. That intellectual error can be countered only by a body of thought that is better rooted in realistic assumptions on the aspirations and limitations of human nature and the day-to-day working of political institutions that are tested by experience in history . . . But much more has to be done, not least by the re-emerging of private services to demonstrate from their day-to-day activities that they can better the state. And their demonstration will have to be supplemented by devising techniques for enabling *all* the people, not only the moneyed or the higher-paid worker, to pay. The ability to pay is the key to the development of private services in all forms. The IEA [Institute of Economic Affairs] is setting in train a 3-year study that merits wide support to examine the scope for reconstructing the edifice of state benefits to this end. Such devices – reverse taxes, tax credits, vouchers, etc. – must precede, or at least run in parallel with, expansion in the scope for private entrepreneurship in education, medical supplies and financing, housing, possibly pensions, and a host of smaller services. There would then be a faster growth in life assurance for school fees, BUPA-type [private health] insurance, saving for house purchase, and insured pension schemes and annuities.

A. Seldon, *Wither the Welfare State*, 1981, pp. 25–6 and 43–4.

Questions
1. *What does Seldon identify as the most damaging area of the welfare state? Why does he single out this area?*
2. *Describe his blueprint for the development of social policy.*
3. *Why do you think the author regards the means test as a sensitive and humane way of distributing benefits?*

These policy options have received serious attention within the Conservative Party. Perhaps the most widely canvassed has been the possibility of dismantling the NHS and replacing it with private medicine financed through private insurance. This fee-for-service system of health care could operate in a number of ways. First, it could be financed through private insurance, in which individuals are responsible for choosing their own company and level of cover; the arrangement adopted by most of those using private medicine in Britain at the moment. For people unable to afford the insurance premiums, the state would provide a safety-net of care. This two-tier apparatus is similar to the health care system operating in the USA, with Medicare providing some cover for the 24 million aged and Medicaid attempting to give financial assistance with the health bills of the 20 million poor. A second method of funding private medicine is also based on insurance, but a public scheme of personal insurance. Compulsory health insurance provides the basis of West Germany's health care system and over 90 per cent of the population are covered. The government itself lays down the minimum benefit package and the maximum contributions.

A shift to health insurance would bring health care into line with social security. Both would operate on a two-door system of access, one for those whose premiums covered the cost of care, the other for those who, without adequate insurance, would be admitted on a means-tested basis.

The Royal Commission on the National Health Service looked at these alternative methods of financing the service in 1979. Their conclusions are contained in the passage below.

Reading 5

There are two important disadvantages which arise in most insurance based schemes. First, there are groups in the community who are both bad health risks and too poor to pay high premiums. They include elderly people, children, and the mentally and physically handicapped. Over 60% of NHS expenditure is currently accounted for by these groups, and nearly half of the community are exempted for one good reason or another from prescription charges, for example. Poorer people tend to have worse health, but they are of course also least able to pay insurance and are most likely to be deterred by charges at time of use. The imbalance between ability to pay for health care and the need for it is met in most countries by government support. However, an insurance scheme which offered a range of benefits according to ability to pay would inevitably favour the wealthier members of society . . . The introduction of an insurance system would incorporate into the NHS a new principle, namely that a different standard of health care under the NHS was available to those who chose to pay for it. Some may feel such a change to be desirable, but at least it should be clearly recognised for what it is.

The second disadvantage is the cost of administration. The bulk of NHS funds are collected through general taxation. No special mechanism is required. An insurance system would require insurance companies to determine premiums, collect them and distribute them in the form of payment for services either to the claimant or to the hospital or practitioner who had provided the treatment. A mechanism for helping those too poor to pay premiums would be needed. It seems to us that this would inevitably lead to more forms to fill in and more people to handle them.

Royal Commission on the National Health Service, 1979, pp. 337–8.

Questions
1. *What makes someone a 'bad health risk'? Why are those who are bad health risks also likely to be poor?*
2. *According to the Royal Commission, what effects would the introduction of an insurance system have on the NHS and on patients?*

The final reading identifies other problems with the New Right's blueprint for social policy. It suggests that its view of redistribution is a narrow one, concerning the distribution of income among wage-earners and between wage-earners and claimants. The reading suggests, further, that the liberal view of dependency is too narrow, seeing dependency as a short-term condition for people who would otherwise earn their own living. Finally, the reading argues that the liberal view of poverty is too narrow and unacceptable in a society which seeks to provide all its citizens with an adequate quality of life.

Reading 6
For the New Right, society often seems to be composed of adult men in good health. In its many discussions of income distribution, problems of distribution between adult men in work and women with children who are out of the labour force are rarely mentioned. Yet there is no mechanism within the market economy which will ensure a reasonable share of income for

dependent groups. Governments in many countries have had to face these issues both because of the decline of the extended family and because views on the rights of women and children have changed. Government policy on the distribution of income has sprung more from *these* issues of distribution [between wage-earners and dependants] than from the pure redistribution from the rich to the poor which the New Right so dislikes . . .

Discussion about redistribution cannot be merely abstract; it also has to take into account the basic requirements for sustaining family life in an economy in which the family is vulnerable to disruption and to economic change. The New Right would confine definition of poverty to the absolute sense of the term – the minimum required to allow physical subsistence. But there are serious reasons for doubting whether poverty as a relative concept – a standard depending upon what is common in a particular period – can be dismissed quite so sweepingly . . . The most serious objection . . . is to the ethical view inherent in the New Right's definition of poverty. It implies that society has an interest in maintaining the lives of its members on a purely physiological or animal basis but does not care about whether people's ability to function mentally and socially is maintained. This would seem to be less than humane to people who are not able to re-enter the labour market – the elderly and the disabled. Life is not merely physiological existence: it is also about relationships, activity and dignity. The stress of dependence may, in any case, threaten relationships and induce depression. But if, as well as being dependent, people have to struggle to maintain even the barest pretence of a normal existence in society, integrity, and even survival, will be further threatened. For people who will re-enter the labour market, an absolute definition of poverty becomes a poor business proposition as well as inhumane. It implies that society should be indifferent to their future potential for independence. Thus, rejection of the relative definition involves a view of human life which is both short-sighted and profoundly dispiriting.

N. Bosanquet, *After the New Right*, 1983, pp. 116–17.

Questions

1. *Explain why Bosanquet argues that 'there is no mechanism within the market economy which will ensure a reasonable share of income for dependent groups'.*

2. *What does his argument suggest about the living standards of (a)*

*women, (b) school leavers, (c) pensioners dependent on state benefits,
in a society organised around liberal principles?*

3. *In Bosanquet's view, how do market liberals define poverty?*

4. *How might a market liberal reply to Bosanquet's criticisms of the New
Right?*

The readings in this chapter raise many of the issues with which
the book has been concerned. They highlight the issues, but they
do not resolve them. It is to be hoped that they provide a greater
insight into the controversies which have engaged sociologists
working in the field of health and welfare. It is hoped, too, that
the readings in this and the previous chapters have helped
develop opinions as well as understandings about health, welfare
and social policy.

ESSAY QUESTIONS

1. Examine the ways in which the different perspectives by sociologists
   influence their definition and explanation of social problems and also
   their interpretation of social policies to deal with such problems.
   (JMB, 1980)

2. Discuss the social significance of an 'ageing population'. (AEB,
   specimen paper)

3. *Universalism* (the principle that benefits are provided on the basis of
   right, irrespective of the claimant's situation) and *selectivism* (the
   principle that benefits are provided on the basis of the financial
   position of the recipient) are often given as alternative approaches to
   welfare provision. What are the objectives of universalistic and
   selective welfare provisions? Are the two incompatible? (JMB, 1981)

4. Discuss the case for and against replacing the National Health Service
   with personal health insurance and private medicine.

5. Using examples, examine the relationship between sociology and
   social policy. (AEB, 1982)

6. Examine *two* explanations of the 'crisis' in the welfare state.

7. Examine the implications of the claim that 'a society's problems are
   defined in the political arena'. In what other contexts, and by which
   other people, are social problems defined? (JMB, 1982)

FURTHER READING

1. New Society Studies Reader, *New Directions in Social Policy*, New
   Society, 1982. Articles by D. Donnison on 'A radical strategy to help
   the poor' and B. Abel-Smith, 'Towards a healthier population'.
   Donnison's article describes the priorities for an attack on poverty:

reducing unemployment, improving the living standards of the low paid, and increasing supplementary benefit scale rates. Abel-Smith looks at future health policies and identifies some problems with self-help and personal responsibility.

2. R. Harris and A. Seldon, *Over-ruled on Welfare*, Institute of Social and Economic Affairs, 1979, pp. 1–3 and 183–200.

Identifies the failure of the welfare state and of the quest for equality through social policy. Outlines a liberal policy on welfare, emphasising the principle of charging for services to maintain standards, maximise choice and reduce costs.

3. P. Townsend and N. Davidson, *Inequalities in Health*, Penguin, 1982, pp. 173–205.

Adopting a materialist perspective, Townsend and Davidson argue that health inequalities cannot be eliminated solely through the NHS. They present a strategy to combat unemployment, poverty, environmental danger, work hazards and poor housing.

4. A. Seldon (ed), *The Litmus Papers: A National Health Service*, Centre for Policy Studies, 1980.

Presents the case against the NHS and proposes the development of private medicine, based on personal insurance, in its place.

5. A. Coote and B. Campbell, *Sweet Freedom: The Struggle for Women's Liberation*, Pan Books, 1982, pp. 235–48.

Presents a feminist programme for social policy, covering employment and equal pay, social security and the family.

List of references

CHAPTER 1

R. Dingwall, *Aspects of Illness*, Martin Robertson, 1976.

I. Kennedy, *Unmasking Medicine*, Allen and Unwin, 1981.

D. Tuckett, *An Introduction to Medical Sociology*, Tavistock, 1976.

L. Doyal, 'A matter of life and death: medicine, health and statistics' in J. Irvine, I. Miles and J. Evans (eds), *Demystifying Social Statistics*, Pluto Press, 1979.

B.S. Rowntree, *Poverty and Progress*, Longman, 1941.

J. Kincaid, *Poverty and Inequality in Britain*, Penguin, 1973.

P. Townsend, 'Measuring poverty', *British Journal of Sociology*, 1954, 5, 130–7.

CHAPTER 2

T. McKeown, *The Role of Medicine*, Basil Blackwell, 1979.

G. Newman, *Infant Mortality: A Social Problem*, Methuen, 1906.

Department of Health and Social Security, *Prevention and Health*, Cmnd.7047, HMSO, 1977.

O. Lewis, *La Vida: A Puerto Rican Family in the Culture of Poverty – San Juan and New York*, Penguin, 1965.

P. Townsend and N. Davidson, *Inequalities in Health*, Penguin, 1982.

R. Holman, 'Another model of poverty' in E. Butterworth and R. Holman (eds), *Social Welfare in Modern Britain*, Fontana, 1975.

CHAPTER 3

M. Gray, *Neurosis: A Comprehensive Critical View*, Van Nostrand Reinhold, 1978.

T. Szasz, 'The myth of mental illness', *American Psychologist*, 1960, 15, 113–18.

M. Piercy, *Woman on the Edge of Time*, Women's Press, 1976.

G. Brown, 'Depression: a sociological view' in D. Tuckett and J. Kaufert (eds), *Basic Readings in Medical Sociology*, Tavistock, 1978.

S. Lipshitz, 'Women and psychiatry' in J. Chetwynd and O. Hartnett (eds), *The Sex Role System*, Routledge and Kegan Paul, 1978.

CHAPTER 4

P. Townsend, 'The structured dependency of the elderly', *Ageing and Society*, 1981, March, 5–28.

B. Gilbert, *The Evolution of National Insurance in Great Britain*, Michael Joseph, 1973.

C. Jones, *State Social Work and the Working Class*, Macmillan, 1983.

J. Mayer and N. Timms, *The Client Speaks: Working Class Impressions of Casework*, Routledge and Kegan Paul, 1970.

N. Timms, *The Receiving End: Consumer Accounts of Social Help to Children*, Routledge and Kegan Paul, 1973.

T. Robinson, *In Worlds Apart: Professionals and their Clients in the Welfare State*, Bedford Square Press, 1978.

M. Spring-Rice, *Working Class Wives: their Health and Conditions*, Penguin, 1939 (republished by Virago, 1981).

CHAPTER 5

C. Pond and J. Popay, 'Tackling inequalities at their source' in H. Glennerster (ed), *The Future of the Welfare State*, Heinemann, 1983.

J. Le Grand, *The Strategy of Inequality*, Allen and Unwin, 1982.

Brent Community Health Council, *Black People and the Health Service*, Brent CHC, 1981.

R. Klein, 'International perspectives on the NHS', *British Medical Journal*, 1977, 2, 1492–3.

A. Seldon, *Wither the Welfare State*, Institute of Economic Affairs, 1981.

I. Illich, *Medical Nemesis*, Calder and Boyars, 1975.

CHAPTER 6

M. Friedman, *Capitalism and Freedom*, University of Chicago Press, 1962.

N. Ginsberg, *Class, Capital and Social Policy*, Macmillan, 1979.

H. Land, 'Sex role stereotyping in the social security and income tax system' in J. Chetwynd and O. Hartnett (eds), *The Sex Role System*, Routledge and Kegan Paul, 1978.

R. Titmuss, *Commitment to Welfare*, Allen and Unwin, 1968.

R. Titmuss, *The Gift Relationship*, Allen and Unwin, 1970.

CHAPTER 7

R. Moroney, *The Family and the State: Considerations for Social Policy*, Longman, 1976.

A. Walker, 'Caring for elderly people: a conflict between women and the state' in J. Finch and D. Groves (eds), *A Labour of Love: Women, Work and Caring*, Routledge and Kegan Paul, 1983.

M. Anderson, 'What is new about the modern family: an historical perspective' in British Society for Population Studies, *The Family*, Office of Population, Censuses and Surveys, 1983.

Equal Opportunities Commission, *Caring for the Elderly and Handicapped: Community Care Policies and Women's Lives*, EOC, 1982.

V. Macleod, *Whose Child?*, Study Commission on the Family, 1983.

N. Timms, *The Receiving End: Consumer Accounts of Social Help for Children*, Routledge and Kegan Paul, 1973.

CHAPTER 8

A. Sinfield, 'The necessity for full employment' in H. Glennerster, *The Future of the Welfare State*, Heinemann, 1983.

M. David and H. Land, 'Sex and social policy' in H. Glennerster, *The Future of the Welfare State*, Heinemann, 1983.

R. Harris, 'Economic effects of moral hazard' in H. Parker, *The Moral Hazard of Social Benefits*, Institute of Economic Affairs, 1982.

A. Seldon, *Wither the Welfare State*, Institute of Economic Affairs, 1981.

Royal Commission on the National Health Service, Cmnd.7615, HMSO, 1979.

N. Bosanquet, *After the New Right*, Heinemann, 1983.

Bibliography

R. Boyson (ed), *Down With the Poor*, Churchill Press, 1971.

G. Brown and T. Harris, *The Social Origins of Depression*, Tavistock, 1978.

A. Cartwright and M. O'Brien, 'Social class variations in health care and the nature of general practitioner consultations' in M. Stacey (ed), *The Sociology of the National Health Service*, Sociological Review Monograph 22, University of Keele, 1976.

P. Chesler, *Women and Madness*, Allen Lane, 1972.

Commission of the European Community, *Perceptions of Poverty*, Commission of the European Community, 1977.

G. Davies and D. Piachaud, 'Social policy and the economy' in H. Glennerster (ed), *The Future of the Welfare State*, Heinemann, 1983.

A. Deacon and J. Bradshaw, *Reserved for the Poor: The Means Test in British Social Policy*, Basil Blackwell and Martin Robertson, 1983.

Equal Opportunities Commission, *Seventh Annual Report: 1982*, Equal Opportunities Commission, 1983.

E. Evans (ed), *Social Policy, 1830–1914*, Routledge and Kegan Paul, 1978.

M. Friedman and R. Friedman, *Free to Choose*, Secker and Warburg, 1980.

V. George, *Social Security and Society*, Routledge and Kegan Paul, 1973.

E. Goffman, *Stigma*, Penguin, 1968.

E. Goffman, *Asylums*, Penguin, 1970.

P. Golding and S. Middleton, *Images of Welfare: Press and Public Attitudes to Welfare*, Martin Robertson, 1982.

N. Hart, 'Understanding debates about health inequality', paper presented at the Joint Meeting of Health Economists and Medical Sociologists, University of York, 1983.

B. Jordan, *Poor Parents*, Routledge and Kegan Paul, 1974.

N. Keddie, *Tinker, Tailor . . . The Myth of Cultural Deprivation*, Penguin, 1973.

R. Littlewood and M. Lipsedge, *Aliens and Alienists: Ethnic Minorities and Psychiatry*, Penguin, 1982.

T. Parsons, *The Social System*, Routledge and Kegan Paul, 1951.

B.S. Rowntree, *Poverty: A Study in Town Life*, Macmillan, 1901.

P. Sedgwick, *Psycho Politics*, Pluto Press, 1982.

A. Smith, *Inquiry into the Nature and Causes of the Wealth of Nations* (originally pub. 1776), Everyman, 1910.

J. Stern, 'Social mobility and the interpretation of social class mortality differentials', *Journal of Social Policy*, 1983, 12, 27–49.

J. Stuart Mill, *Principles of Political Economy* (originally pub. 1848), Penguin, 1970.

M. Swenarton, *Homes Fit for Heroes*, Heinemann, 1981.

R.H. Tawney, *Religion and the Rise of Capitalism*, Penguin, 1938.

Index